D1571312

IEEE Recommended Practice for Grounding of Industrial and Commercial Power Systems

Published by
The Institute of Electrical and Electronics Engineers, Inc

Distributed in cooperation with
Wiley-Interscience, a division of John Wiley & Sons, Inc

ANSI/IEEE
Std 142-1982
(Revision of ANSI/IEEE
Std 142-1972)

An American National Standard

IEEE Recommended Practice for Grounding of Industrial and Commercial Power Systems

Sponsor

**Power System Technologies Committee
of the
IEEE Industry Applications Society**

Approved June 10, 1982

IEEE Standards Board

Approved February 4, 1983

American National Standards Institute

Second Printing
September 1986

ISBN 0-471-89573-3

Library of Congress 82-083209

© Copyright 1982 by

The Institute of Electrical and Electronics Engineers, Inc
345 East 47th Street, New York, NY 10017, USA

September 17, 1982   *SH08797*

When the IEEE Standards Board approved this standard on June 10, 1982, it had the following membership:

Foreword

(This Foreword is not a part of ANSI/IEEE Std 142-1982, IEEE Recommended Practice for Grounding of Industrial and Commercial Power Systems.)

This recommended practice is a revision of IEEE Std 142-1972. The subjects covered by this document are divided into four parts corresponding to the four sections.

Section 1 covers the problems of system grounding, that is, connection to ground of the neutral, of the corner of the delta, or of the midtap of one phase. The advantages and disadvantages of grounded versus ungrounded systems are discussed. Information is given on how to ground the system, where the system should be grounded, and how to select equipment for the grounding of the neutral circuits.

Section 2 deals with the problems of connecting the frames and enclosures of electric apparatus, such as motors, switchgear, transformers, buses, cables, conduits, building frames, and portable equipment, to a ground system. It also outlines the fundamentals of making the inter-connection or ground-conductor system between electric equipment and the ground rods, water pipes, etc.

Section 3 deals with the problems of static electricity—how it is generated, what processes may produce it, how it is measured, and what should be done to prevent its generation or to drain the static charges to earth to prevent sparking. The methods of protecting structures against the effects of lightning are also covered; since the system for protecting structures against lightning consists entirely of conductors to earth, it is considered within the scope of this document to discuss the general aspects of the problem.

Section 4 deals with the problems of obtaining a low-resistance connection to the earth. The use of ground rods, connections to water pipes, etc, are discussed.

Looking at the problem from an overall standpoint, the grounding of the system would in most cases be done by making a metallic connection directly or through an impedance between transformer or generator neutrals and the building grounding system that is described in Section 2. The grounding system described in Section 2 in turn is connected to earth through the system of ground rods and water pipes described in Section 4.

The protective system for static and lightning protection discussed in Section 3 would likewise be connected to the ground rods and water pipe system, as outlined in Section 4.

The major revisions are contained in Section 3, with only minor changes in Sections 1, 2, and 4.

This recommended practice was reviewed and approved by the Power Systems Technologies Committee of the IEEE Industry Applications Society. This revision was prepared by the Power Systems Grounding Subcommittee, of the Power Systems Technologies Committee. At the time it approved this recommended practice, the subcommittee had the following membership:

L. J. Kelly, Chairman

Baldwin Bridger
Thad Brown
Edward Cantwell
Leonard S. Corey
J. W. Courter
D. C. Grant
Gordon S. Johnson

Richard H. Kaufman
Ralph H. Lee
Robert Loewe
Bal K. Mathur
William J. Neiswender
Elliot Rappaport
Mark T. Theriault

Donald W. Zipse

Grounding of Industrial and Commercial Power Systems

4th Edition

Working Group Members and Contributors

L. J. Kelly, *Chairman*

Chapter 1 — Systems Grounding: J. W. Courter
Chapter 2 — Equipment Grounding: Leonard J. Kelly
Chapter 3 — Static and Lightning Protection Grounding: Bal K. Mathur
Chapter 4 — Connection to Earth: Baldwin Bridger

Contents

FIGURES

1. System Grounding

1.1 Introduction. Whether or not to ground an electrical system is a question that must be faced sometime by most engineers charged with planning electrical distribution. A decision in favor of a grounded system leads to the question of how to ground.

It is the purpose of this section to assist the planning engineer in answering these and other more detailed questions on the subject by presenting basic reasons for grounding or not grounding and by reviewing general practices and methods of system grounding.

Practices of the grounding of synchronous generators [7][1] and of distribution and transmission systems [9], particularly those operated at 23 kV and higher, have been summarized in other guides. The practices set forth in those guides are applicable to industrial power systems to various degrees, depending on the type and extent of the industrial system under consideration and on the character of service required at the points of power consumption.

Where an industrial power system consists of power-generating equipment, transmission circuits, and distribution circuits, the reasons for grounding these components are often the same as those for grounding similar components of public utility systems and other large power systems, and the methods of grounding would generally be similar under like conditions of service. But in some cases the reasons for grounding and the methods of grounding certain components of an industrial power system may differ according to the requirements of manufacturing or process operations.

The National Electrical Code [2], sponsored by the National Fire Protection Association, contains regulations pertaining to system and equipment grounding applicable to industrial, commerical, and health-care facilities. These

---

[1] The numbers in brackets correspond to those of the references listed in 1.15.

rules are considered minimum requirements for the protection of life and property and should be carefully reviewed during the course of system design.

1.2 Definitions. Definitions of terms in addition to those appearing in this section may be found in ANSI/IEEE Std 100-1977 [1].

The varieties of system grounding are the following.

ungrounded system. A system, circuit, or apparatus without an intentional connection to ground, except through potential-indicating or measuring devices or other very-high-impedance devices.

NOTE: Though called ungrounded, this type of system is in reality coupled to ground through the distributed capacitance of its phase windings and conductors. In the absence of a ground fault, the neutral of an ungrounded system under reasonably balanced load conditions will usually be close to ground potential, being held there by the balanced electrostatic capacitance between each phase conductor and ground. Figure 1(a) shows an ungrounded system with voltage relations for balanced phase-to-ground capacitance.

grounded system. A system of conductors in which at least one conductor or point (usually the middle wire or neutral point of transformer or generator windings) is intentionally grounded, either solidly or through an impedance.

NOTE: Various degrees of groundings are used, from solid or effective grounding to the high-impedance grounding obtained from a small grounding transformer used only to secure enough ground current for relaying, to the high-resistance grounding which secures control of transient overvoltage but may not furnish sufficient current for ground-fault relaying. Figures 1(b) and (c) shows two points at which a system may be grounded and the corresponding voltage relationships. Note that according to NEMA SG 4-1975 [6] there are system voltage limitations for corner grounding.

grounded solidly. Connected directly through an adequate ground connection in which no impedance has been intentionally inserted.

NOTE: This term, though commonly used, is somewhat confusing since a transformer may have its neutral solidly connected to ground, and yet the connection may be so small in capacity as to furnish only a very-high-impedance ground to the system to which it is connected. In order to define grounding positively and logically as to degree, the term *effective grounding* has come into use. The term *solidly grounded* will therefore be used in this standard only in referring to a solid metallic connection from system neutral to ground; that is, with no impedance intentionally added in the grounding circuit.

grounded effectively. Grounded through a sufficiently low impedance such that for all system conditions the ratio of zero-sequence reactance to positive-sequence reactance (X_0/X_1) is positive and less than 3, and the ratio of zero-sequence resistance to positive-sequence reactance (R_0/X_1) is positive and less than 1.

NOTE: The effectively grounded system permits the application of surge arresters with less than line-to-line voltage ratings. Ground fault currents will be approximately of the same magnitude as three-phase fault currents.

resistance grounded. Grounded through impedance, the principal element of which is resistance.

NOTE: The high-resistance-grounded system is designed to meet the criterion of $R_0 \leqslant X_{C0}$ in order to limit transient overvoltages due to arcing ground faults. The ground-fault current is usually limited to less than 10 A. X_{C0} is the distributed per-phase capacitive reactance to ground of the system.

The low-resistance-grounded system permits a higher ground-fault current (on the order of 25 A to several hundred amperes) to obtain sufficient current for selective relay performance. For the usual system the criterion for limiting transient overvoltages is $R_0/X_0 \geqslant 2$.

inductance grounded. Grounded through impedance, the principal element of which is inductance.

NOTE: The conditions of an inductance-grounded system are that X_0/X_1 lie within the range of 3–10 and $R_0/X_0 \leqslant 1$. The ground-fault current becomes 25% or more of the three-phase fault current. Inductance grounding becomes "effective" grounding if X_0/X_1 is reduced to 3 or less.

1.3 Factors Influencing the Choice of Grounded or Ungrounded System

1.3.1 Service Continuity. For many years a great number of industrial plant distribution systems have been operated ungrounded at one or more voltage levels. In most cases this has been done with the thought of gaining an additional degree of service continuity. The fact that any contact occurring between one phase of the system and ground is unlikely to cause an immediate outage to any load may represent an advantage in many plants, varying in its importance according to the type of plant.

Grounded systems, in most cases, are designed so that circuit protective devices will remove a faulty circuit from the system regardless of the type of fault. A phase-to-ground fault generally results in the immediate isolation of the faulted circuit with the attendant outage of the loads on that circuit. However, experience has shown [10], in a number of systems, that greater service continuity may be obtained with grounded-neutral than with ungrounded-neutral systems.

1.3.2 Multiple Faults to Ground. While a ground fault on one phase of an ungrounded system generally does not cause a service interruption, the occurrence of a second ground fault on a different phase, before the first fault is cleared, does result in an outage. If both faults are on the same feeder, that feeder will be opened. If the second fault is on a different feeder, both feeders may be deenergized.

The longer a ground fault is allowed to remain on an ungrounded system, the greater is the likelihood of a second one

occurring on another phase, resulting in an outage. The advantage of an ungrounded system, in not immediately dropping load upon the occurrence of a ground fault, may be largely destroyed by the practice of ignoring a ground fault until a second one occurs and repairs are required to restore service. With an ungrounded system it is extremely important that an organized maintenance program be provided so that ground faults are located and removed as soon as possible after their detection.

An adequate detection system, possibly in conjunction with an audible alarm, is considered essential for operation of an ungrounded system. In addition, it is advisable in ungrounded systems to employ ground-fault tracing equipment which permits maintenance personnel to locate a ground fault with the system energized and without the necessity of interrupting service on any circuit during the process of fault locating.

Experience has shown that multiple ground faults are rarely, if ever, experienced on grounded-neutral systems.

1.3.3 Arcing Fault Burndowns. In recent years, especially in low-voltage power systems, many cases of arcing fault burndowns have been reported in which severe damage to or complete destruction of electrical equipment was caused by the energy of arcing fault currents [15]. In typical cases an arcing fault becomes established between two or more phase conductors in an ungrounded system, or between phase conductor(s) and ground in a solidly grounded-neutral system. The fault arc causes the release of enormous amounts of energy at the fault site, resulting in the violent generation of hot gases and arc plasma. The accompanying heat is so intense that it vaporizes copper or aluminum conductors and surrounding steel enclosures and distills toxic and flammable gases from organic insulation systems. Frequently the devastation is so complete that the equipment involved must be totally replaced [16].

It is characteristic of arcing fault burndowns that the normal phase-overcurrent devices do not operate to remove the initial fault quickly. Arcing fault current levels may be so low that such devices either are not actuated at all (because fault currents are below pickup settings) or are actuated only after a long period of time, too late to prevent burndown.

The low-current arcing faults are characteristic of open or covered buses, particularly in switchgear or metal-enclosed switching or motor control equipment. Instances of burndown have also occurred in high-capacity buses having relatively wide spacing, served from the utility network at 480Y/277 V through protective devices rated 2000 A or larger. Such spacing can limit the current of a single arc to approximately 1500 A, which is not enough to operate the phase protective devices, so arcing continues for many minutes.

It is generally recognized that prevention of arcing fault burndowns, at the present state of protective system design, must rely upon fast and sensitive detection of the arcing fault current, accompanied by an interruption of the faulty circuit within approximately 10–20 cycles. In the solidly grounded-neutral system, this fast sensitive detection is possible since an arcing fault will produce a current in the ground path, either because the fault begins as a line-to-ground fault or because it will almost instantly involve ground, even though initiated as a line-to-line arcing fault. Under normal (nonground fault) conditions

there is no significant current in the ground return path. Therefore, monitoring the solidly grounded-neutral system for currents in the ground circuit provides an easy means for detecting and removing destructive arcing faults to ground. This type of protection is universally applicable throughout the power system, and the sensitivity and speed of such relaying are independent of load current values and phase-overcurrent device settings.

An inherent problem of ground-fault protection devices typically installed in low-voltage main circuit breakers, service breakers, etc, is that a ground fault in a cable or equipment of a small subfeeder or branch of the system is likely to trip the large main circuit breaker, shutting down the entire installation. Nonselective tripping can be a problem unless coordinated ground-fault protection devices are installed at each feeder, subfeeder, and at each load branch of the system. Where isolation of only the faulted portion of a system is important, much care must be used in applying ground-fault protection equipment.

Thus the solidly and low-resistance grounded-neutral systems provide a basis for easily securing protection against ruinous phase-to-ground arcing fault burndowns. (Unfortunately, no comparably reliable and universally applicable means of protection against low-level *line-to-line* arcing fault burndowns has been devised.)

1.3.4 Location of Faults. On an ungrounded system, a ground fault does not open the circuit. Some means of detecting the presence of a ground fault on the system should be installed. Lamps connected to indicate the potential from each phase to ground will show the presence of a ground fault and which phase is involved, but will not show on which feeder the fault has occurred. Locating a ground fault on one of the several feeders may require removing from service one feeder at a time until the ground detector indicates that the faulted feeder has been removed from the system. Should it happen that the same phase of two different feeders becomes faulted to ground at the same time, the faulted feeders cannot be located by removing them from the system one at a time. It may be necessary to remove all feeders and restore them to service one at a time, checking the ground detector as each feeder is restored.

The location of a grounded feeder on an ungrounded system may be facilitated by the use of various types of locating apparatus [13]. For example, an interrupted direct voltage or superimposed audio signal may be applied to the feeder bus and the tracing current detected in the grounded feeders. Some operators have reported success using locating apparatus not requiring deenergizing system feeders [14]. This, of course, has the advantage of permitting the location of ground faults without waiting for light load periods on the system.

An accidental ground fault on a grounded system is both indicated and at least partially located by an automatic interruption of the accidentally grounded circuit or piece of equipment.

1.3.5 Safety. Many of the hazards to personnel and property existing in some industrial electrical systems are the result of poor or nonexistent grounding of electrical equipment and metallic structures. While the subject of equipment grounding is treated in Section 2, it is important to note here that regardless of whether or not the system is grounded, safety considerations require thorough grounding of equipment and structures.

Proper grounding of a low-voltage (600 V or less) distribution system may result in less likelihood of accidents to personnel than when the system is supposedly left ungrounded. The knowledge that a circuit is grounded generally will result in greater care on the part of the worker.

It is erroneous to believe that on an ungrounded system a person may contact an energized phase conductor without personal hazard. As Fig 1(a) shows, an ungrounded system with balanced phase-to-ground capacitance has normal line-to-neutral voltage between any phase conductor and ground. To accidentally or intentionally contact such a conductor may present a serious, perhaps lethal, shock hazard.

While a ground-fault remains on one phase of an ungrounded or impedance-grounded system, personnel contacting one of the other phases and ground are subjected to 1.73 times the voltage that would be experienced on a solidly neutral-grounded system. The voltage pattern is the same as that shown in Fig 1(c).

Other hazards of shock and fire may result from inadequate grounding of equipment in either grounded or ungrounded systems. Accidental ground faults are inevitable. The current path to ground for a winding-to-frame insulation breakdown in a motor may include greasy shavings or other materials that can be ignited by sparks or localized heating. Such a high-impedance ground circuit may not permit enough current flow to operate protective devices, with the result that a potential fire and safety hazard may exist for some time. There is hazard of a shock to personnel from such a condition, should they bridge all or part of the high-impedance ground path, for example by contacting the frame of the faulty machine. This hazard is particularly bad because there are

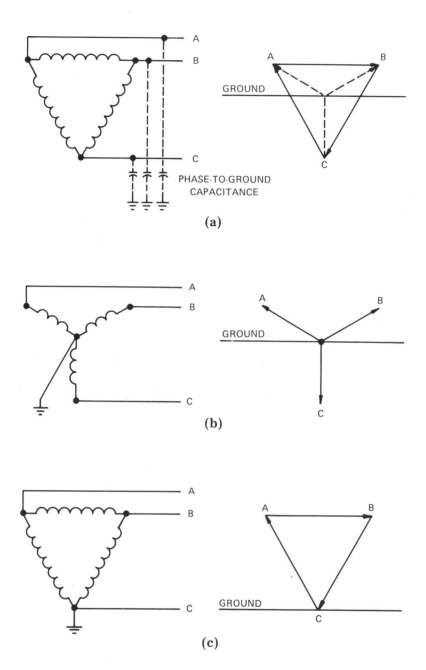

Fig 1
Voltages to Ground under Steady-State Conditions
(a) Ungrounded System (b) Grounded Wye-Connected System
(c) Corner Grounded Delta-Connected System

more possible victims than in the case where persons familiar with electric systems work on a circuit.

On the other hand, the relatively high ground-fault currents associated with solidly grounded systems may present a hazard to exposed workers from hot arc products and flying molten metal, which is not present in ungrounded systems. This problem has become much less serious however, because of the universal use of metal-enclosed equipment.

1.3.6 Abnormal Voltage Hazards. The possible overvoltages on the ungrounded system may cause more frequent failures of equipment than if the system were grounded. In some cases these overvoltages have caused failures on more than one unit of equipment at the same time. These multiple failures are not necessarily confined to one feeder, but may involve equipment on several different feeders.

A fault on one phase of an ungrounded or impedance-grounded system places a sustained increased voltage on the insulation of ungrounded phases in a three-phase system. This overvoltage is 1.73 times the voltage normally on the insulation. This or other sustained overvoltages or the transient overvoltages on the ungrounded system may not immediately cause failure of insulation, but may tend to reduce the life of the insulation.

The reduced overvoltages experienced on grounded systems are less likely to damage equipment or insulation.

1.3.7 Power System Overvoltages (See [11, chap 5]. Some of the more common sources of overvoltage on a power system are the following:
(1) Lightning
(2) Switching surges
(3) Static
(4) Contact with a high-voltage system

(5) Line-to-ground faults
(6) Resonant conditions
(7) Restriking ground faults

1.3.8 Lightning (See Section 3 and [17].) Most industrial systems are effectively shielded against direct lightning strokes. Many circuits are either underground in ducts or within grounded metal conduits or raceways. Even open-wire circuits are often shielded by adjacent metallic structures and buildings. Surge arresters applied at the incoming service limit the surge voltages within the plant which result from strokes to the exposed service lines. Other arrestor applications may be necessary within the plant to protect low-impulse-strength devices such as rotating machines. Where a plant is supplied from a substation stepping down from some higher voltage, surge arresters are desirable on the low side of the transformer, since the leading edge of an incoming surge (prior to the primary arrester flashover point) is transformed just as are the power frequencies. Such a surge pulse is capable of damaging equipment connected to the secondary winding unless surge protective devices suitable for this equipment are applied.

1.3.9 Switching Surges. Normal switching operations in the system can cause overvoltages. These are generally not more than three times normal voltage and of short duration. Overcurrent devices such as circuit breakers or non current-limiting fuses, in general, interrupt a circuit at a normal current zero, at which time the stored energy in the inductance of the circuit is zero. The overvoltages thus developed result from transient oscillation in the circuit capacitance and inductance, there being stored energy in the circuit capacitance at the time of current interruption. More serious overvoltages can be produced by devices which interrupt by forcing current zero. Such devices as vacuum interrupters and current-limiting fuses must be carefully applied because of this overvoltage problem. In low-voltage systems, however, the standards citation for current-limiting fuses require that the maximum peak voltage occurring during circuit interruption shall not exceed 3000 V; this is less than the crest of the normal high-potential test voltage applied to equipment in the 600 V class.

Neutral grounding is not likely to reduce the total magnitude of overvoltage produced by lightning or switching surges. It can, however, distribute the voltage between phases and reduce the possibility of excessive voltage stress on the phase-to-ground insulation of a particular phase.

1.3.10 Static. (See Section 3.) Buildup of overvoltage on power system conductors due to static charge is not usually a problem in modern plants with metal-enclosed circuits and equipment. Static charge on moving belts can build up voltages which can be transmitted to the power system unless motor frames are properly grounded. Overhead open-wire lines may be subject to static overvoltages resulting from certain atmospheric conditions. A system ground connection, even of relatively high resistance, can effectively prevent static voltage buildup.

1.3.11 Contact with Higher Voltage System. Contact with a higher voltage system may be caused by a broken high-voltage conductor falling on a lower voltage conductor where both lines cross or are carried on the same poles, or by breakdown between the high- and low-voltage windings of distribution transformers, causing other failures of insulation, possibly at several points. An effectively grounded low-voltage system, though experiencing high values of fault current for this condition, will hold the system neutral close to ground potential, and thus the overvoltages to ground on the low-voltage system will be greatly reduced.

1.3.12 Line-to-Ground Faults. Common source of sustained overvoltage on an ungrounded system is one phase of a three-phase system becoming grounded. In this case the insulation of the other phases is subjected to a voltage 73% above normal. A solidly grounded-neutral system would not permit this overvoltage. While this voltage seldom approaches the insulation levels of equipment and circuits, the cumulative effect of higher than normal voltage stresses may somewhat reduce insulation life.

1.3.13 Resonant Conditions. An ungrounded system may be subjected to resonant overvoltages. With the high phase-to-ground capacitance of larger systems, there may be a condition of approximate circuit resonance during a line-to-ground fault through an inductance such as a faulty coil in a motor starter. The voltage to ground of the unfaulted phases will then be considerably in excess of line-to-line voltage. An overvoltage due to resonant or near-resonant conditions can be encountered on a small system where tuned inductive-capacitive circuits are used for such purposes as the operation of welders. For example, if the welder is equipped with a series capacitor for power factor improvement, the voltages across the capacitor and across the transformer winding are each many times the supply-line-to-line voltage. A fault between the capacitor and the welder transformer imposes this high voltage on the insulation of the ungrounded system. A grounded-neutral system would prevent this overvoltage by holding the phases to their approximate normal voltages to ground.

1.3.14 Restriking Ground Faults. Field experience and theoretical studies have shown that arcing, restriking, or vibrating ground faults on ungrounded systems can, under certain conditions, produce surge voltages as high as 6 times normal. The conditions necessary for producing these overvoltages require that the dielectric strength of the arc path build up at a higher rate after each extinction of the arc than it did after the preceding extinction. This phenomenon is unlikely to take place in open air between stationary contacts because such an arc path is not likely to develop sufficient dielectric recovery strength. It may occur in confined areas where the gas pressure may increase after each conduction period. Neutral grounding is effective in reducing transient voltage buildup from such intermittent ground faults by reducing neutral displacement from ground potential and the destructiveness of any high-frequency voltage oscillations following each arc initiation or restrike.

1.3.15 Cost. The cost differential between grounded and ungrounded neutral systems will vary, depending on the method of grounding, the degree of protection desired, and whether a new or an existing system is to be grounded.

For the new system in the design stage, power transformers with wye-connected secondaries and wye-connected generators are available as standard options, and there is no cost factor for establishing the system neutral. The additional cost items are the neutral grounding resistor or reactor if the system is to be impedance grounded, and the cost of ground fault relaying.

To ground an existing ungrounded delta-connected system requires an additional cost item, namely, the grounding transformer(s) for establishing the system neutral. Also, the existing protective relay schemes may have to be modified to obtain sensitive ground-fault detection. For the existing system, practical consideration may dictate the application of a high-resistance grounding scheme, with alarm only on the occurrence of a ground fault. This eliminates the requirement for adding sensitive ground current relays to each feeder circuit.

The decision to convert an existing ungrounded system to grounded operation is usually made for the purpose of limiting transient overvoltages. Older systems with cables, and motor and transformer windings that have degraded insulation levels due to aging, atmospheric conditions, and sustained overvoltages are particularly vulnerable to failure due to transient overvoltages resulting from arcing ground faults. Therefore the cost for converting to grounded operation is small when compared to the cost of possibly having to replace cables or rewind motor or transformers.

1.3.16 Trends in the Application of System Grounding. The basic reasons for system grounding are the following.

(1) To limit the difference of electric potential between all uninsulated conducting objects in a local area

(2) To provide for isolation of faulted equipment and circuits when a fault occurs

(3) To limit overvoltages appearing on the system under various conditions

Many industrial power system operators believe that an ungrounded system offers greater service continuity than a grounded system, because a line-to-ground fault does not cause immediate tripping of the faulted circuit. On the other hand, a second ground fault on another phase of a circuit other than that where the original fault occurred causes a phase-to-phase fault, large short-circuit current flow (with attendant hazards), and tripping of both faulted circuits. Also, the effect of sporadic low-level arcing, at the first failure location, produced by the capacitive "grounding" currents from the two ungrounded phases, may cause the whole system-to-ground voltage to rise to 4 or more times normal voltage (to ground), causing severe stress on all of the insulation. It is such an overstress that can cause the failure at a second location, almost concurrent with the first failure. The various grounding systems eliminate this phenomenon by changing the fault current from entirely capacitive to something nearer a true resistive current.

Consequently, a major factor to consider in selecting a grounded or ungrounded system is the quality of electrical maintenance available. Well-maintained ungrounded systems, in which the first ground fault is promptly located and corrected, probably have greater service continuity than solidly grounded systems. However, many users whose maintenance practices are not quite so extensive feel that a grounded-neutral system gives them more continuous service than an ungrounded system.

There has been an increasing trend toward grounding industrial systems in order to overcome some of the disadvantages attributed to ungrounded operation. In recent years a substantial percentage of new industrial substation transformers have been purchased with wye-connected low-voltage windings, with the insulated neutral brought to external termination suitable for neutral grounding.

In new installations these transformers offer the advantage that they can be operated ungrounded, while having the neutral available for grounding, if desired, at some future time.

1.4 Methods of System Gounding

1.4.1 Grounding the System Neutral.
Most grounded systems employ some method of grounding the system neutral at one or more points. These methods (Fig 2) are referred to as the following:

Solid grounding
Resistance grounding
Reactance grounding
Ground-fault-neutralizer grounding

Each method, as named, refers to the nature of the external circuit from system neutral to ground rather than to the degree of grounding. In each case the impedance of the generator or transformer, whose neutral is grounded, is in series with the external circuit. Thus a solidly grounded generator or transformer may or may not furnish effective grounding to the system, depending on its impedance.

1.4.2 Solid Grounding.
Solid grounding refers to the connection of the neutral of a generator, power transformer, or grounding transformer directly to the station ground or to the earth. Because of the reactance of the grounded generator or transformer in series with the neutral circuit, a solid ground connection does not provide a zero-impedance neutral circuit.

If the reactance of the generator or transformer is too great with respect to the total system reactance, the objectives sought in grounding, principally freedom from transient overvoltages, may not be achieved. Thus it is necessary to determine the degree of grounding provided in the system. A good guide in answering this question is the magnitude of ground-fault current as compared to the system three-phase current. The higher the ground-fault current in relation to the three-phase fault current the greater the degree of grounding in the system. In terms of resistance and

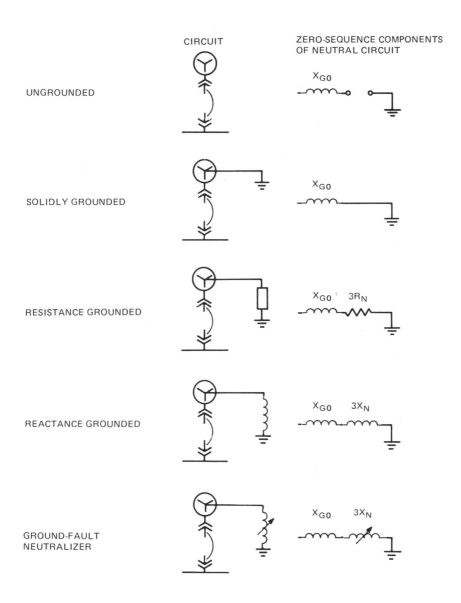

X_{GO} = Zero-sequence reactance of generator or transformer
X_N = Reactance of grounding reactor
R_N = Resistance of grounding resistor

Fig 2
System Neutral Circuit and Equivalent Diagrams for Ungrounded
and Various Types of Grounded-Neutral Systems

reactance, effective grounding of a system is accomplished only when $R_0 \leqslant X_1$ *and* $X_0 \leqslant 3X_1$, and such relationships exist at any point in the system. The X_1 component used in the above relation is the Thévenin equivalent positive-sequence reactance of the complete system including the subtransient reactance of all rotating machines.

In most generators solid grounding, that is, without external impedance, may permit the maximum ground-fault current from the generator to exceed the maximum three-phase fault current which the generator can deliver and for which its windings are braced. Consequently, neutral-grounded generators should be grounded through an impedance which will limit the ground-fault current to a value no greater than the generator three-phase fault current. In the case of three-phase four-wire systems, the limitation of ground-fault current to 100% of the three-phase fault current is usually practical wtihout interfering with normal four-wire operation.

Surge arresters for grounded-neutral service (rated near but not less than 80% of line-to-line voltage) require that the system be effectively grounded. This will carry with it a line-to-ground circuit current of at least 60% of the three-phase short-circuit value.

1.4.3 Resistance Grounding. In resistance grounding the neutral is connected to ground through one or more resistors. In this method, with the resistor values normally used, and except for transient overvoltages, the line-to-ground voltages that exist during a line-to-ground fault are nearly the same as those for an ungrounded system.

A system properly grounded by resistance is not subject to destructive transient overvoltages. For resistance-grounded systems at 15 kV and below,

such overvoltages will not ordinarily be of a serious nature if the resistance value lies within the following boundary limits: $R_0 \leqslant X_{C0}$, $R_0 \geqslant 2X_0$. The corresponding ground-fault current is far less than is normally used for low-resistance grounding, but is the design criterion for high-resistance grounding.

Resistance grounding may be either of two classes, high resistance or low resistance, distinguished by the magnitude of ground-fault current permitted to flow. Both types are designed to limit transient overvoltages to a safe level (within 250% of normal). However, the high-resistance method usually does not require immediate clearing of a ground fault since the fault current is limited to a very low level. This low level, typically on the order of 5 A, must be at least equal to the system total capacitance-to-ground charging current. The protective scheme associated with high-resistance grounding is usually detection and alarm rather than immediate tripout. In general the use of high-resistance grounding on systems where the line-to-ground fault current exceeds 10 A should be avoided because of the damage potential of an arcing current larger than 10 A in a confined space.

The low-resistance method has the advantage of immediate and selective clearing of the grounded circuit, but requires that the minimum ground-fault current be large enough to positively actuate the applied ground-fault relay. High-resistance grounding is a method that can be applied to existing medium-voltage ungrounded systems to obtain the transient overvoltage protection without the modification expense of adding ground relays to each circuit.

Systems grounded through resistors require surge arresters suitable for use on ungrounded-neutral circuits, that is, with a voltage rating at least equal to the line-to-line voltage.

The reasons for limiting the current by resistance grounding may be one or more of the following:

(1) To reduce burning and melting effects in faulted electric equipment, such as switchgear, transformers, cables, and rotating machines

(2) To reduce mechanical stresses in circuits and apparatus carrying fault currents

(3) To reduce electric-shock hazards to personnel caused by stray ground-fault currents in the ground return path

(4) To reduce the arc blast or flash hazard to personnel who may have accidentally caused or who happen to be in close proximity to the ground fault

(5) To reduce the momentary line voltage dip occasioned by the occurrence and clearing of a ground fault

(6) To secure control of transient overvoltages while at the same time avoiding the shutdown of a faulty circuit on the occurrence of the first ground fault (high-resistance grounding)

1.4.4 Reactance Grounding. The term *reactance grounding* describes the case in which a reactor is connected between the system neutral and ground. Since the ground-fault current that may flow in a reactance-grounded system is a function of the neutral reactance, the magnitude of the ground-fault current is often used as a criterion for describing the degree of grounding. In a reactance-grounded system, the available ground-fault current should be at least 25% and preferably 60% of the three-phase fault current to prevent serious transient overvoltages ($X_0 \leqslant 10X_1$). This is considerably higher than the level of fault current desirable in a resistance-grounded system, and therefore, reactance grounding is usually

not considered an alternative to resistance grounding.

In practice, reactance grounding is generally used only in the case cited in 1.4.2, in which a generator neutral is to be connected to provide four-wire service. In this event it may be necessary to add a low-value reactor to limit the available ground-fault current through the generator to a value no greater than the three-phase fault current contributed by the generator.

1.4.5 Ground-Fault Neutralizer (Resonant Grounding) (See [8].) A ground-fault neutralizer is a reactor connected between the neutral of a system and ground and having a specially selected, relatively high value of reactance.

A line-to-ground fault causes line-to-neutral voltage to be impressed across the neutralizer, which passes an inductive current. This current is $180°$ out of phase and is approximately equal in magnitude (when the neutralizer is tuned to the system) to the resultant of system charging current of the two unfaulted phases. The inductive and capacitive components of current neutralize each other, and the only remaining current in the fault is due to resistance, insulator leakage, and corona. This current is relatively small, and since it is in phase with the line-to-neutral voltage, the current and voltage pass through a zero value at the same instant. In addition, the rate of rise of the recovery voltage on the faulted phase is very low. Therefore the arc is extinguished without restriking, and flashovers are quenched without removing the faulted line section from service. It should be noted that failures in solid insulations such as paper, varnished cambric, and rubber are not self-healing as insulator flashovers are, and not extinguished by the use of the ground-fault neutralizer.

On systems for which faults in air are relatively frequent, ground-fault neutralizers may be very useful by reducing the number of circuit breaker operations required to remove faults, thus improving service continuity. They have been used primarily on systems above 15 kV, consisting largely of overhead transmission or distribution lines. This method is a second choice to resistor grounding, which provides ground relaying to disconnect the faulted circuit.

In some cases, where it has not been deemed desirable by the plant operators to trip a circuit on the occurrence of a ground fault, special arrangements have been used to limit the damage due to the flow of charging current and yet be able to easily locate the faulty feeder. One method is to use a ground-fault neutralizer in the neutral to limit the ground-fault current and to reduce switching surges to safe values. In some cases it may be desirable to pass enough ground-fault current to operate relays that give a signal or trip the circuit breaker of the faulty feeder. This is done by a current-sensing relay in combination with a resistor in parallel with the neutralizer. Because of the current to be switched, a power circuit breaker should be used for switching the resistor. The resistor and relay are selected as if only the resistor were used. Such a scheme is expensive and is employed only in very special cases.

One of the disadvantages of resonant-grounded systems is that care must be taken to keep the ground-fault neutralizer tuned to the system capacitance to minimize the development of transient overvoltages. Thus when sections of the system are switched on or off, it may be necessary to adjust the neutral reactance by changing the neutralizer tap. This can be accomplished by providing an ammeter and a control switch for remote control of a motor-driven tap changer on the neutralizer, so that when parts of the system are switched, the neutralizer can be readjusted. Because of those complications, the ground-fault neutralizer is very rarely used in industrial and commercial systems.

1.4.6 Grounding at Points Other than System Neutral. In some cases low-voltage systems (600 V and below) are grounded at some point other than the system neutral. This has been done to obtain a grounded system at a minimum expense where existing delta transformer connections do not provide access to the system neutral.

1.4.7 *Corner-of-the-Delta* **Grounding.** In low-voltage systems, which in the past have nearly all been supplied from transformers with delta-connected secondaries, grounding of one phase, *(corner-of-the-delta)* grounding has sometimes been used as a means of obtaining a grounded system. Advantages are the following:

(1) Possible cost advantage over other grounding methods for existing delta systems

(2) Possibility of slightly better protection with two-element motor starters when they are located in the two ungrounded phases; with properly connected circuits, ground-faults in the control circuit will neither start the motor nor prevent stopping the motor by means of the push button

Disadvantages are the following:

(1) An inability to supply dual-voltage service for lighting and power load

(2) The necessity of positive identification of the grounded phase throughout the system to avoid connecting meters, instruments, and relays in the grounded phase

(3) A higher line-to-ground voltage on

two phases than in a neutral-grounded system

(4) The possibility of exceeding interrupting capabilities of marginally applied circuit breakers, because for a ground fault, the interrupting duty on the affected circuit breaker pole exceeds the three-phase fault duty

Because of its limitations, this type of grounding has not been widely used in industrial systems.

1.4.8 One Phase of a Delta System Grounded at Midpoint. Where existing systems at 600 V and below are supplied by three single-phase transformers with midtaps available, it is possible to gain some of the advantages of neutral grounding by grounding the midtap of one phase. This method does not provide all the advantages of system neutral grounding. Such connections are also used to obtain a limited amount of 240/120 V single-phase power in a three-phase 240 V system.

1.5 Selection and Design of System Grounding Arrangements

1.5.1 Obtaining the System Neutral. The best way to obtain the system neutral for grounding purposes in three-phase systems is to use source transformers or generators with wye-connected windings. The neutral is then readily available. Such transformers are available for practically all voltages except 240 V. On new systems, 208Y/120 or 480Y/277 V wye-connected transformers may be used to good advantage instead of 240 V. Wye-connected source transformers for 2400, 4160, and 13 800 V systems are available as a standard option, whereas 4800 and 6900 V wye-connected source transformers may be priced at a premium rate. The alternative is to apply grounding transformers.

1.5.2 Grounding Transformers. System neutrals may not be available, particu-

larly in many old systems of 600 V or less and many existing 2400, 4800, and 6900 V systems. When existing delta-connected systems are to be grounded, grounding transformers may be used to obtain the neutral. Grounding transformers may be of either the zigzag, the wye-delta, or the T-connected type. One type of grounding transformer commonly used is a three-phase zigzag transformer with no secondary winding. The internal connection of the transformer is illustrated in Fig 3. The impedance of the transformer to balanced three-phase voltages is high so that when there is no fault on the system, only a small magnetizing current flows in the transformer winding. The transformer impedance to zero-sequence voltages, however, is low so that it allows high ground fault currents to flow. The transformer divides the ground fault current into three equal components; these currents are in phase with each other and flow in the three windings of the grounding transformer. The method of winding is seen from Fig 3 to be such that when these three equal currents flow, the current in one section of the winding of each leg of the core is in a direction opposite to that in the other section of the winding on that leg. This tends to force the ground-fault current to have equal division in the three lines and accounts for the low impedance of the transformer-to-ground currents.

A wye–delta-connected three-phase transformer or transformer bank can also be utilized for system grounding. As in the case of the zigzag grounding transformer, the usual application is to accomplish resistance-type grounding of an existing ungrounded system. The delta connection must be closed to provide a path for the zero-sequence current, and the delta voltage rating is selected for

31

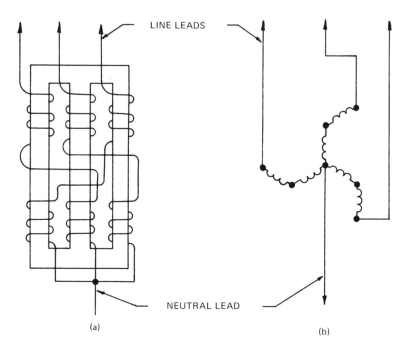

LINE LEADS

NEUTRAL LEAD

(a)

(b)

Fig 3
(a) Core Windings (b) Connections of Three-Phase
Zigzag Grounding Transformer

any standard value. A resistor inserted between the primary neutral and ground, as shown in Fig 4, provides a means for limiting ground-fault current to a level satisfying the criteria for resistance-grounded systems. For this arrangement, the voltage rating of the wye winding need not be greater than the normal line-to-neutral system voltage. For high-resistance grounding it is sometimes more practical or economical to apply the limiting resistor in the secondary delta connection. Three single-phase distribution class transformers are used, with the primary wye neutral connected directly to ground. The secondary delta is closed through a resistor which effectively limits the primary ground-fault current to the desired low level. For this

alternative application, the voltage rating of each of the transformer windings forming the wye primary should not be less than the system line-to-line voltage.

The rating of a grounding transformer, in kilovoltamperes, is equal to the rated line-to-neutral voltage in kilovolts times the rated neutral current. Most grounding transformers are designed to carry their rated current for a limited time only, such as 10 s or 1 min. Consequently they are much smaller in size than an ordinary three-phase continuously rated transformer with the same rating.

It is generally desirable to connect a grounding transformer directly to the main bus of a power system, without intervening circuit breakers or fuses, to prevent the transformer from being in-

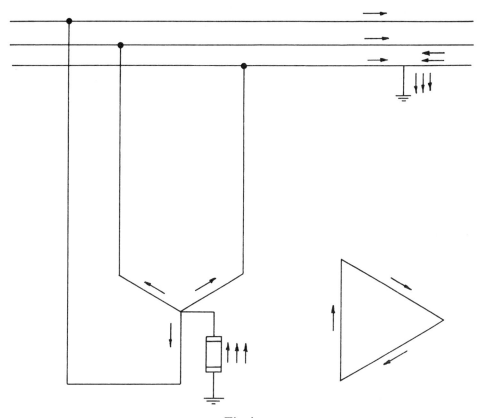

Fig 4
Vectors Representing Current Flow in Wye–Delta Transformer
Used as Grounding Transformer with Line-to-Ground Fault

advertently taken out of service by the operation of the intervening devices. (In this case the transformer is considered part of the bus and is protected by the relaying applied for bus protection.) Alternatively the grounding transformer should be served by a dedicated feeder circuit breaker, as shown in Fig 5(a), or connected between the main transformer and the main switchgear as illustrated in Fig 5(b). If the grounding transformer is connected as shown in Fig 5(b), there should be one grounding transformer for each delta-connected bank supplying power to the system, or enough ground-

ing transformers to assure at least one grounding transformer on the system at all times. When the grounding transformer is so connected, it is included in the protective system of the main transformer.

1.5.3 Suggested Grounding Methods for Systems 600 V and below. Low-voltage systems are frequently operated solidly grounded. The principal reason for this is the extensive use of 480 Y/277 V systems with line-to-neutral connected loads, and the requirement in the National Electrical Code,

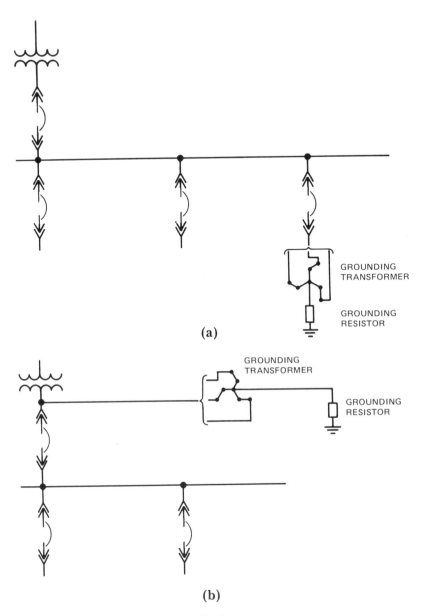

(a)

(b)

Fig 5
**Methods of Connecting Grounding Transformer to a Delta-Connected or
Ungrounded Power System to Form Neutral for System Grounding**

ANSI/NFPA 70-1981 [2] for solidly grounding the neutral of such systems.

For the low-voltage system without line-to-neutral loading, solid grounding or high-resistance grounding are the practical choices. Low-resistance grounding is usually not considered since it would require the use of sensitive ground-fault protective devices throughout the system. For reasons of economy the solidly grounded system depends on adequate ground-fault current at locations remote from the source to operate phase fault devices. It is therefore especially important that the equipment grounding network provide a very-low-impedance return path for the ground-fault current. High-resistance system grounding, with alarm only, can be used if service continuity is of prime importance and if the faulted circuit can be located and isolated with little delay.

1.5.4 Systems 2.4-15 kV. Modern power systems in this range of voltages are usually low-resistance grounded to limit the damage due to ground faults in the windings of rotating machines and yet permit sufficient fault current for the detection and selective isolation of individual faulted circuits.

Ground faults are detected by an overcurrent relay connected in the residual circuit of the three-phase current transformers (Fig 6), or by a relay connected to a window- or doughnut-type (zero-sequence) current transformer which encloses all the phase conductors (Fig 7). When any loads are connected line to neutral, then the window-type current transformers must also enclose the neutral conductor. Using either method, positive tripping can be accomplished with low magnitudes of ground-fault current. However, the sensitivity of the residual scheme is limited by the relatively high ratios of phase current transformers, so greater sensitivity is available with the zero-sequence current transformer method. For this reason low-resistance grounding is commonly used, except for those cases where the size of the system is so small that the maximum available fault current is not high enough to be objectionable.

Alternatively, high-resistance grounding, as discussed in 1.4.3, can be used.

This contributes to better service continuity by permitting continued operation with one ground fault. However, it does so at the sacrifice of selectivity in ground-fault protection, because the fault current is normally too low to allow use of time-overcurrent relays.

At the present time there are 2.4 kV systems in operation without the system neutral grounded. More and more engineers, however, are applying system neutral grounding to 2.4 kV systems. The conventional method is to provide sufficient ground-fault current to permit selective relaying through the application of ground relays.

1.5.5 Systems above 15 kV. Systems above 15 kV are nearly always effectively grounded, because these are usually circuits with open lines in which surge arresters rated for grounded neutral service are desirable for better overvoltage protection and lower cost. These may be either distribution or transmission circuits. Recent trends are toward higher voltages for distribution [19]. In addition, rotating equipment is seldom connected directly to these systems; hence limiting ground-fault currents to prevent the burning of laminations is a less important factor than in lower voltage systems. In addition, voltages above 15 kV are not usually carried inside buildings, hence personnel hazards due to high fault currents are not a factor. Finally, the cost of resistors for resistance grounding at these voltages is prohibitive.[2]

---

[2] In recent years, electric utility distribution voltages above 15 kV have become quite common. Utility distribution networks above 15 kV are almost invariably effectively grounded; this must be considered when designing the primary distribution system of an industrial or commercial facility which is supplied at these voltages. If resistance grounding is desirable, a delta-wye transformation between the utility and the user system is usually used to provide zero-sequence isolation of the latter.

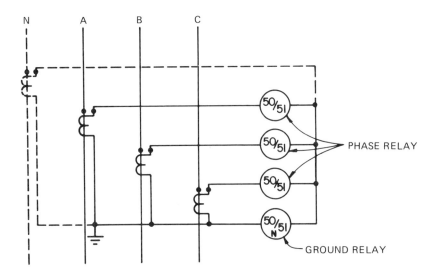

Fig 6
Ground-Fault Detection Diagram Using
Overcurrent Relay in Residual Circuit

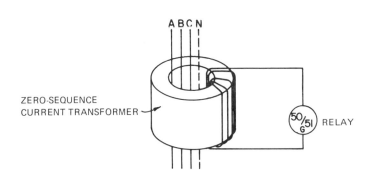

Fig 7
Ground-Fault Detection Diagram Using Overcurrent Relay Connected
to Zero-Sequence (Doughnut) Current Transformer

1.5.6 Criteria for Limiting Transient Overvoltages. (See [12].) Transient overvoltages can be limited effectively to safe values if the following criteria are observed:

(1) In resistance-grounded systems the resistor ground-fault current should be at least equal to, but preferably greater than, the charging current of the system.

(2) In reactance-grounded systems the ratio of X_0/X_1 should be 10 or less, where X_0 is the zero-sequence inductive reactance of the system, including that of the neutral reactance, and X_1 is the positive-sequence inductive reactance of the system, including the subtransient reactance of all rotating machines.

(3) Where a combination of grounding transformer and neutral-grounding resistor is used, the grounding transformer impedance should be low relative to the neutral resistance. The ratio of R_0/X_0 should be equal to or greater than 2, where R_0 is the zero-sequence resistance of the circuit, including the neutral resistor, and X_0 is the zero-sequence inductive reactance of the circuit, including that of the transformer and resistor.

1.6 Selection of System Grounding Points

1.6.1 Ground at Each Voltage Level. Delta–wye or wye–delta transformers effectively block the flow of zero-sequence current between systems. Hence it is necessary to ground at each voltage level to achieve the advantages of neutral grounding in all parts of the system. Each voltage level may be grounded at the neutral lead of a generator, power transformer bank, or grounding transformer. Any generator or transformer used for grounding should, as far as possible, be one that is always connected to the system. Alternatively, a sufficient number of generators or transformers should be grounded to ensure at least

one ground connection on the system at all times.

1.6.2 Ground at the Power Source and Not at the Load. The use of an available neutral at a load point, such as a wye-delta step-down transformer or a wye-connected motor, is not recommended as a point for system grounding. The principal disadvantage is that a number of these load neutrals must be grounded to ensure that the system remains grounded if one or more of these loads is out of service.

Consequently, the ground-fault current may be excessively high when all grounded points are in service. Since power sources are fewer in number than loads and are less likely to be disconnected, they are preferred as grounding points. Other disadvantages of grounding at the load are the following:

(1) Standard low-voltage unit substations have delta-connected primaries; therefore special transformers are required if the primaries are to be used as grounding points.

(2) Since the ground-fault current is dependent on the number of feeders or grounding points in operation, it may vary widely depending on system operating conditions. This makes selective relaying more difficult and may require additional directional ground relaying to avoid false tripping of healthy feeder circuits.

(3) The windings of many motors are not braced to withstand the unbalanced forces associated with ground faults

1.6.3 Ground Each Major Source Bus Section. When there are two or more major source bus sections, each section should have at least one grounded-neutral point, since the bus tie circuit may be open. If there are two or more power sources per bus section, there should be provision for grounding at least two sources on each section. For four-wire distribution systems, grounding of the neutral conductor requires special consideration for reasons of safety and proper detection of ground fault (see IEEE Std 242-1975 [4] and [18].

1.6.4 Neutral Circuit Arrangements. When the method of grounding and the grounding point have been selected for a particular power system, the next question to consider is how many generator or transformer neutrals will be used for grounding and whether (1) each neutral will be connected independently to ground, or (2) a neutral bus with a single ground connection will be established.

1.6.5 Single Power Source. When a power system has only one source of power (generator or transformer), grounding may be accomplished by connecting the source neutral to earth either directly or through a neutral impedance. Provision of a switch or circuit breaker to open the neutral circuit is not necessary because neutral circuits have parctically zero potential with respect to ground, except during the short interval of a fault; hence breakdowns are not likely. Also, it is not desirable to operate the system ungrounded by having the ground connection open while the generator or transformer is in service. In addition, the neutral switching equipment greatly increases the cost of grounding.

In the event that some means of disconnecting the ground connection is required in a particular case, a metalclad circuit breaker should be used rather than an open disconnect switch for indoor installations. The latter is hazardous to personnel if a ground fault should occur while the switch is being opened or closed.

1.6.6 Multiple Power Sources. For installation involving two or three generators or power transformers individual neutral impedances are frequently used. With this arrangement the neutral of each generator or main transformer bank is connected directly to its neutral impedance without intervening switching equipment. No special operating instructions are required since each impedance is automatically connected whenever its source is connected. In the case of resistance grounding, each resistor rating should be based on providing sufficient current for satisfactory relaying when its source is operating independently, and also to limit the total ground current when the sources are paralleled.

When total ground-fault currents with several individual resistors would exceed about 1000–4000 A, neutral switchgear and a single resistor should be considered for resistance-grounded systems.

When individual resistors are used, circulation of third-harmonic currents between paralleled generators is not a problem since the resistance limits the circulating current to negligible values.

When there are more than two or three generators or power-supply transformer banks at one installation, it is economically desirable to use only one resistor. Each power source is then connected to the resistor through a neutral bus and neutral switching equipment. This arrangement keeps the ground-fault current to a practical minimum, since the ground current from the station is never greater than what can be supplied through a single resistor. It also ensures the same value of ground current regardless of the number of generators or transformers in use and simplifies ground relaying.

The primary purpose of the neutral circuit breakers is to isolate the generator or transformer neutrals from the neutral bus when the source is taken out of service, because the neutral bus is energized during ground faults.

Circuit breakers are preferred to disconnecting switches for indoor installations to ensure safety to personnel. If disconnecting switches are used, as in some outdoor installations, they should be elevated or metal enclosed and interlocked in such a manner as to prevent their operation except when the transformer primary and secondary switches or generator main and field circuit breakers are open.

It is sometimes desirable to operate with only one generator neutral circuit breaker closed at a time to eliminate any circulating harmonic or zero-sequence currents. When the generator whose neutral is grounded is to be shut down, another generator is grounded by means of its neutral circuit breaker before the main and neutral circuit breakers of the first one are opened. However, with similar generators and reasonably equal load division, circulating currents are negligible, and it is often found practical to operate with neutral circuit breakers of two or more generators closed. This simplifies operating procedure and increases assurance that the system will be grounded at all times. In the case of multiple transformers, all neutral isolating devices may be normally closed because the presence of delta-connected windings (which are nearly always present on at least one side of each transformer) minimizes the circulation of harmonic current between transformers.

When only one source is involved, but others are to be added to the station in the future, space should be allowed to add neutral switchgear when this becomes necessary.

1.7 Calculation of Ground-Fault Currents

1.7.1 General. The magnitude of the current that will flow in the event of a line-to-ground fault on a grounded system is determined by the impedance from the source to the fault plus the impedance of the ground return path, including the impedances of grounding transformers, resistors, and reactors. For interconnected systems the calculation of the current may be rather complicated. For simpler cases an approximation of the available fault current may be obtained.

1.7.2 Resistance Grounding. When a single line-to-ground fault occurs on a resistance-grounded system, a voltage appears across the resistor (or resistors) nearly equal to the normal line-to-neutral voltage of the system.

In low-resistance grounded systems the resistor current is approximately equal to the current in the fault. Thus the current is practically equal to the line-to-neutral voltage divided by the resistance used in ohms. Standard grounding resistors have a voltage rating equal to the line-to-neutral voltage and a current rating equal to the current that flows when this voltage is applied to the resistor. Thus, for example, a maximum ground-fault current of approximately 1000 A will be obtained on a system when using a 1000 A resistor. This very simple method of calculating the ground-fault current is only suitable when the ground-fault current is small compared to the three-phase fault current.

The method just outlined applies to faults on lines or buses or at the terminals of machines or transformers. If the fault is internal to a rotating machine or transformer, the ground-fault current will be less. The reduction in current is primarily due to the internal voltage of the apparatus. In the case of wye-connected equipment, this internal voltage is at full value at the terminals and is zero at the neutral. If the fault occurs at the neutral of any apparatus, no voltage will appear across the system grounding resistor, so the fault current will be zero. At intermediate points in the winding between the neutral and a terminal, the fault current will be intermediate between zero and the current due to a terminal fault. For example, at a point 10% of the winding length from neutral, the ground-fault current will be approximately 10% of the value for a terminal fault. For a fault anywhere between this point and a terminal, the current will be more than 10% of the amount for a terminal fault.

In the case of the delta-connected machines, the internal voltage to neutral may be considered to be 100% at the terminals and 50% at the midpoint of the windings. The midpoints have the lowest potential with respect to the electric neutral of any part of the winding. Therefore a ground fault at any point in the winding will produce a ground-fault current of 50% or more of the line-terminal fault value.

1.7.3 Reactance Grounding. In a reactance-grounded system with a single line-to-ground fault, the ground-fault current may be computed from the following expression, where resistance may usually be neglected:

$$I_g = \frac{3E}{X_1 + X_2 + X_0 + 3(X_n + X_{GP})} \quad \text{(Eq 1)}$$

where

I_g = ground-fault current, in A

X_1 = system positive-sequence reactance, in Ω per phase, including the subtransient reactance of rotating machines

X_2 = system negative-sequence reactance, in Ω per phase, including the subtransient reactance of rotating machines

X_0 = system zero-sequence reactance, in Ω per phase

X_n = reactance of neutral grounding reactor, in Ω

X_{GP} = reactance of ground return circuits, in Ω

E = line-to-neutral voltage in V

In most industrial and commercial systems without in-plant generation X_2 can be considered equal to X_1.

1.7.4 Solid Grounding. In a system with solid neutral connection to ground, the ground-fault current for a single line-to-ground fault may be computed from the following equation:

$$I_g = \frac{3E}{X_1 + X_2 + X_0 + 3X_{GP}} \quad \text{(Eq 2)}$$

1.8 Selection of Grounding Equipment Ratings. (See IEEE Std 32-1972 [3].

1.8.1 General. Grounding resistors, reactors, and grounding transformers are normally rated to carry current for a limited time only. The standard time interval rating usually applicable for industrial systems, with relays arranged to protect the grounding equipment, is 10 s.

The voltage rating of a grounding resistor should be the line-to-neutral voltage rating of the system.

The insulation class of a reactor is determined by the system line-to-neutral voltage. The voltage rating may be less than the line-to-neutral voltage and is calculated by multiplying the rated current by the impedance of the reactor.

The voltage rating of a grounding transformer should be not less than the system line-to-line voltage if the neutral is connected directly to ground or the system line-to-neutral voltage if a resistor is inserted between neutral and ground.

Grounding resistors are rated in terms of the current that will flow through the resistor with the system line-to-neutral voltage applied.

The rated current of a grounding reactor is the thermal current rating. It is the root-mean-square neutral current, in amperes, that the reactor will carry for its rated time without exceeding standard temperature limitations.

If a grounding transformer neutral is solidly connected to ground, the current that will flow during a ground fault is primarily determined by the reactances of the grounding transformer and the system to which it is connected. When a resistor is used between neutral and ground, the current rating of the grounding transformer is based on the resistor rated current. In either case the transformer is rated to carry the required current for rated time without exceeding its rated temperature limits. Many system grounding devices are short-time rated. Care must be exercised in their application to ensure that the current will be automatically interrupted before the thermal limits of the components are exceeded.

1.8.2 Resistor Ratings. For low-resistance grounded-neutral systems the determination of the resistor value, in ohms, and thus the magnitude of the ground-fault current, is based on the following:

(1) Providing sufficient current for satisfactory performance of the system relaying scheme

(2) Limiting ground-fault current to a value that will minimize damage at the point of fault without resulting in system overvoltages.

In most cases the ground-fault current is limited by the neutral resistor to a value considerably less than that which would flow for a three-phase fault. To determine the minimum ground-fault current required, a diagram of the sys-

tem must be available, giving the ratings of current transformers and types of relays for each circuit. This diagram should include consideration of future changes.

The magnitude of the ground-fault current must be sufficient for the operation of all relays that furnish ground-fault protection. In general, if the current is high enough to operate the relays on the higher capacity circuits, it will be adequate for the smaller circuits. As a general rule, ground-fault relays applied on circuits energizing wye-connected machines or transformer windings should operate positively with as little as 10% of the available ground-fault current flowing. For circuits energizing delta-connected machines or transformer windings, and for *upstream* relaying protecting lines or cables, the desired sensitivity is at least 50% of the available fault current. Where differential relays are applied for machine, transformer, bus, or line protection, their sensitivity to ground faults should meet the above criteria unless more sensitive detection is provided by other relays.

Note that the ground-fault current under all system-operating conditions must equal or exceed the minimum required for relaying each circuit connected to the system. This value is established by selecting the highest of those currents that meet the requirements of the several conditions stated above.

1.8.3 Reactor Ratings. The reactance of a neutral-grounding reactor should be chosen to limit the ground current and the current in the faulted phase to the desired value. In order to minimize transient overvoltages, the ground-fault current must not be less than 25% of the three-phase fault current. This corresponds to a ratio of $X_0/X_1 = 10$, where X_0 and X_1 represent the total electrical system values for any possible ground-fault condition on the system. For reactance grounding of generators, the current in any winding must not exceed the three-phase fault current. This corresponds to a ratio of $X_0/X_1 \geqslant 1$, where X_0, and X_1 represent generator reactance only. This establishes the criteria for the maximum and minimum values of neutral reactance. If the neutral reactance is selected in accordance with the following relationship, the current in the winding of the faulted phase will not exceed the three-phase fault current of the machine, regardless of system reactance [11, chaps 5–7]:

$$X_n = \frac{X_1 - X_{G0}}{3} \qquad \text{(Eq 3)}$$

where

X_n = reactance of neutral reactor
X_1 = generator positive-sequence subtransient reactance
X_{G0} = generator zero-sequence reactance

However, the current that flows through the generator neutral reactor itself is not independent of the system constants and may often exceed the three-phase fault current of the machine. The current rating of a neutral reactor is determined by the number and characteristics of the system sources and whether they are grounded or ungrounded.

This rating can be calculated from Eq 1.

The neutral-grounding reactor should be selected to carry the available current under all practical operating conditions. With any given condition of connected grounded-neutral sources, the addition of ungrounded-neutral sources and loads will increase the current flow through the grounded-neutral connections.

1.8.4 Grounding-Transformer Ratings. The electrical specifications of a grounding transformer are the following:

Voltage   The line to-line-voltage of the system

Current   The maximum neutral current

Time   The transformer is usually designed to carry rated current for a short time, such as 10 or 60 s; for high-resistance grounding, the rating may need to be continuous

Reactance   This quantity is a function of the positive-sequence short-circuit reactance of the power system, or X_1

The determination of the grounding-transformer reactance, when used to effect reactance-type grounding, is based on the following criterion. The X_0/X_1 ratio should not exceed 10, and preferably not exceed 3, in order to eliminate the possibility of transient overvoltages from a forced current zero interruption. This maximum limitation of 3 for the X_0/X_1 ratio, together with a maximum limitation of 1 for the R_0/X_1 ratio, will also satisfy the criteria for an effectively grounded system, and will permit the application of line-to-ground-voltage rated surge arresters for greater economy and protection. The ratios specified must be met at any location in the system where the reduced-rating arresters are to be applied. In a system having a grounding transformer, its reactance is the principal part of X_0 in the preceding criterion. Also, the positive-sequence reactance X_1 is equal to the reactance of the system to initial symmetrical root-mean-square three-phase short-circuit current. The value of X_1 used in these limiting ratios should be based on the subtransient reactance of rotating machines and the system configuration or connections that will result in the maximum available three-phase short-circuit current.

In a system otherwise ungrounded, the grounding-transformer reactance X_{gt} in ohms per phase, required to provide any specified X_0/X_1 ratio is given by the following expression:

$$X_{gt} = \frac{1000 \, E_L^2 \, (X_0/X_1)}{kVA_{SC}} \qquad \text{(Eq 4)}$$

where

E_L = line-to-line voltage.
kVA_{SC} = system symmetrical 3-phase, short-circuit capacity in kVA

When a grounding transformer is solidly grounded, care should be taken that its reactance is selected at a value low enough to provide sufficient fault current for tripping relays and circuit breakers.

1.9 Influence of Grounding Method on Control Circuit Safety in System 600 V and Below.
Frequently the safety of a control circuit is offered as a reason for a particular method of grounding. In all cases where motor starter control circuits lack control power transformers, there are potential problems with regard to circuit arrangement which must be considered in order to minimize operating difficulties and personnel hazards. Accidental motor starting due to faulty control circuits may be associated with ungrounded systems as well as with most types of grounded systems.

1.10 Autotransformers.
Power autotransformers are quite frequently used in electric utility power transmission and distribution systems. Their use in industrial power systems as part of the power distribution system is relatively infre-

quent. Autotransformers are quite common, however, in control and utilization equipment. Power systems using autotransformers may be subject to dangerous fundamental-frequency overvoltage during system faults or to high-frequency or steep-wave-front transient overvoltages originating from lightning or switching surges. Solidly grounding the autotransformer neutral will stabilize the system neutral and prevent excessive voltage stresses in the event of ground faults. The disadvantages of solid-neutral grounding is the third-harmonic currents and telephone interference may become excessive in certain cases. These harmonic problems can be minimized by the use of a tertiary delta on the autotransformer.

1.11 Systems with Utility Supply.
Some industrial systems are directly connected at their operating voltage to utility systems. When this is the case, the scheme of grounding the industrial system should be properly coordinated with that for the utility system.

If two systems are interconnected by means of a transformer bank, at least one winding of the bank will normally be connected in delta, and this delta-connected winding will make each system independent from the standpoint of grounding.

1.12 Unit-Connected Generators.
Generators with unit-connected transformers usually are equipped with high-resistance neutral grounding for the following purposes:

(1) To minimize transient overvoltages

(2) To provide a positive indication of a ground fault

(3) To limit ground-fault current to a value low enough to permit an orderly shutdown of the generator without risking severe arc damage.

As in any other high-resistance grounded system, the grounding resistor is chosen to provide a ground-fault current at least as great as the system capacitive charging current.

Depending on the system voltage and ground current, it may be more economical to ground the generator neutral through the primary of a distribution-type transformer with a low-voltage high-current resistor on the secondary than to ground the neutral directly through a high-voltage low-current resistor. When a distribution transformer is used, its primary voltage should be no less than the line-to-neutral voltage of the generator. In fact, to decrease the transformer-magnetizing inrush current on the occurrence of a ground fault, a transformer rated for full line-to-line voltage is often used. In all cases, the zero-sequence circuit design should respect the boundary limit of $R_0 \leqslant X_{C0}$.

Ground faults are detected in this scheme either by a current relay in series with the grounding resistor or by a voltage relay in parallel with the resistor. If the voltage-relay sensor is chosen, possible false operation on third-harmonic voltage, sometimes present, can be avoided by the use of a third-harmonic voltage attenuation filter. In either case, no coordination with relays elsewhere in the power system is needed.

The physical size of the grounding transformer is influenced by the expected duration of ground current. If the generator will be operated with a ground fault for several hours, the transformer should be rated to carry ground current continuously. However, the short-time overload capacity of transformers permits a considerably smaller and less expensive transformer to be used if the generator is tripped off the line immediately or promptly after a fault is detected.

1.13 Three-Phase Four-Wire Systems. In these systems single-phase loads are connected between phase conductors and the neutral conductor. The neutral conductor is insulated over its entire length, except where it is grounded at its source of supply. The neutrals of such systems should be grounded such that during a ground fault the voltage between any phase conductor and ground does not appreciably exceed the normal line-to-ground voltage. Four-wire systems should thus be effectively grounded in such a manner that the ground-fault currents are approximately equal to three-phase fault currents. This is usually accomplished by direct connection of transformer bank neutrals to ground without any intentional neutral impedance.

1.14 Systems with Emergency or Standby Power Sources. See IEEE Std 446-1980 [5, Sec 7] for a detailed discussion on the grounding of emergency and standby power sources. Alternate sources of power for supplying loads essential to the safety of life and property or for critical process continuity may consist of a standby supply from the utility company or on-site generator sets. The transfer of load to the alternate source is usually accomplished automatically through the use of transfer switches or circuit breakers. The design of such systems should ensure the continuity of equipment and system grounding and the detection of ground faults when either source is in use and meet the minimum requirements of the National Electrical Code, ANSI/NFPA 70-1981 [2].

1.15 References

[1] ANSI/IEEE Std 100-1977, Dictionary of Electrical and Electronics Terms.[3]

[2] ANSI/NFPA 70-1981, National Electrical Code.[4]

[3] IEEE Std 32-1972, Terminology and Test Procedure for Neutral Grounding Devices.

[4] IEEE Std 242-1975, Recommended Practice for Protection and Coordination of Industrial and Commercial Power Systems (IEEE Buff Book).

[5] IEEE Std 446-1980, Recommended Practice for Emergency and Standby Power Systems for Industrial and Commercial Applications (IEEE Orange Book).

[6] NEMA SG 4-1975, Alternating Current High-Voltage Circuit Breakers.[5]

[7] AIEE COMMITTEE REPORT. Application Guide for the Grounding of Synchronous Generator Systems. *AIEE Transactions (Power Apparatus and Systems)*, vol 72, June 1953, pp 517-526.[6]

[8] AIEE COMMITTEE REPORT. Application of Ground-Fault Neutralizers. *Electrical Engineering*, vol 72, July 1953, p 606.

[9] AIEE COMMITTEE REPORT. Application Guide on Methods of Neutral Grounding of Transmission Systems. *AIEE Transactions (Power Apparatus and Systems)*, vol. 72, Aug 1953, pp 663-668.

[10] ARBERRY, J.P.E. The Use of 600-Volt Power Systems with Grounded Neutrals. *Proceedings of the AIEE National Power Conference*, Pittsburgh, PA, Apr 1950.

[11] BEEMAN, D.L., Ed. *Industrial Power Systems Handbook*, New York: McGraw-Hill, 1955.

[12] *Electrical Transmission and Distribution Reference Book*, 4th ed., Westinghouse Electric Corporation, East Pittsburgh, PA, 1964, chaps 14 and 19.

[13] FORBES, B.G. Location Grounds on 480-Volt, 3-Phase Delta Systems. *Power Generation*, Sept 1949, pp 60-61.

[14] FOX, F.K., GROTTS, H.J., and TIPTON, C.H. High Resistance Grounding of 2400-Volt Delta Systems with Ground-Fault Alarm and Traceable Signal to Fault. *IEEE Transaction on Industry and General Applications*, vol IGA—1, Sept/Oct 1965, pp 366–372.

[15] KAUFMANN, R.H., and PAGE, J.C. Arcing-Fault Protection for Low-Voltage Power Distribution Systems— Nature of the Problem. *AIEE Transactions (Power Apparatus and Systems)*, vol 79, June 1960, pp 160–167.

[16] SHIELDS, F.J. The Problem of Arcing Faults in Low-Voltage Power Distribution Systems. *IEEE Transactions on*

[3] This standard is published by The Institute of Electrical and Electronics Engineers, Inc. Copies are also available from the Sales department of American National Standards Institute, 1430 Broadway, New York, NY 10018.

[4] The National Electrical Code is published by the National Fire Protection Association, Batterymarch Park, Quincy, MA 02269. Copies are also available from the Sales department of American National Standards Institute, 1430 Broadway, New York, NY 10018.

[5] NEMA publications are available from the National Electrical Manufacturers Association (NEMA), 2101 L. Street, NW, Washington, DC 20037.

[6] For information on the AIEE Committee Reports contact Engineering Societies Library, 345 East 47th Street, New York, NY 10017.

Industry and General Applications, vol IGA-3, Jan/Feb 1967, pp 15–25.

[17] VAUGHAN, H.R. Protection of Industrial Plants Against Insulation Breakdown and Consequential Damage. *AIEE Transactions*, vol 65, Aug/Sept 1946, pp 592–596.

[18] WEST, R.B. Grounding for Emergency and Standby Power Systems. *IEEE Transactions on (Industry Applications)*, vol 1A-15, Mar/Apr 1979, pp 124–136.

[19] ANSI C84.1-1977, Voltage Rating for Electricity Power Systems and Equipment (60 Hz).

1.16 Bibliography

ANSI C2-1981, National Electrical Safety Code.

ANSI/NFPA 78-1980, Lightning Protection Code.

BAKER, D.S. Charging Current Data for Guesswork-Free Design of High-Resistance Grounded Systems. *IEEE Transactions* on Industry Applications , vol IA-15, Mar/Apr 1979, pp 136–140.

BARNETT, H.G. Why Ground Low-Voltage Distribution Systems? *Mill and Factory*, May 1951.

BEEMAN, D.L. System Neutral Grounding in Industrial Plants. *Proceedings of the AIEE National Power Conference*, Pittsburgh, PA, Apr 1950.

BLOOMQUIST, W.C. Grounding of Industrial Systems, *General Electric Review*, Aug 1951.

BRERETON, D.S., and HICKOK, H.N. System Neutral Grounding for Chemical Plant Power Systems. *AIEE Transactions (Applications and Industry)*, vol 74, Nov 1955, pp 315–320.

CASTENSCHIOLD, R. Grounding of Alternate Power Sources. *IEEE Conference Record* 77 CHG 1246-B-IA, Oct 1977, pp 67–72.

JOHNSON, A.A. Grounding Principles and Practice—III: Generator-Neutral Grounding Devices. *Electrical Engineering*, vol 64, Mar 1945, pp 92–99.

STRONG, W.F. Neutral Versus Corner-of-the-Delta Grounding. *Electrical World*, Sept 25, 1950.

THACKER, H.B. Grounded Versus Ungrounded Low-Voltage AC Systems. *Iron and Steel Engineer*, Apr 1954, p 6572.

2. Equipment Grounding

2.1 Basic Objectives

2.1.1 General. Equipment grounding, in contrast with system grounding, relates to the manner in which nonelectrical conductive material, which either encloses energized conductors or is adjacent thereto, is to be interconnected and grounded. The basic objectives being sought are the following:

(1) To ensure freedom from dangerous electric-shock-voltage exposure to persons in the area

(2) To provide current-carrying capability, both in magnitude and duration, adequate to accept the ground-fault current permitted by the overcurrent protection system without creating a fire or explosive hazard to building or contents

(3) To contribute to superior performance of the electrical system.

2.1.2 Voltage Exposure. Industry electric accident statistics compiled by the State of California make it clearly evident that many personal injuries are caused by electric shock as a result of making contact with metallic members that are normally not energized and normally can be expected to remain nonenergized. Effective equipment grounding practices would eliminate these personal injuries [9].[7]

Where there is unintentional contact between an energized electrical conductor and the metal frame or structure that encloses it (or is adjacent), the frame or structure tends to become energized to the same voltage level as exists on the energized conductor. To oppose this tendency and to avoid the appearance of a dangerous exposed shock-hazard voltage, the equipment grounding conductor must present a low-impedance path from the stricken frame to the zero-potential reference ground junction at the source entrance equipment (or adjacent to the source machine

------

[7]The numbers in brackets correspond to those of the references listed in 2.10.

of a separately derived electrical system originating within the building).

The impedance of the grounding conductor must be low enough to accept the full magnitude of line-to-ground fault current without creating an impedance (IZ) voltage drop large enough to be dangerous. It is clear that the magnitude of the available ground-fault current of the supply system will have a direct bearing on the ground-conductor requirements.

2.1.3 Avoidance of Thermal Distress. In addition to accomplishing an acceptably low value of electric-shock-voltage exposure, the grounding conductor must function to conduct the full ground-fault current (magnitude and duration) without excessively raising the temperature of the grounding conductor or causing the expulsion of sparks or arcs that could initiate a fire or an explosion. The use of a large-cross-section grounding conductor of itself is not enough. It must be installed so that the total impedance of the fault circuit, including the grounding conductor, will permit the required current amplitude to cause operation of the protective system. The installation must also provide a more favorable (lower impedance) fault return path than other possible paths which might have inadequate current-carrying capacity.

Summaries of the industrial claim insurance of fire insurance companies indicate that approximately one out of every seven fires in industrial establishments originates in electric systems. While these reports undoubtedly contain some unjustified assignments under the category of merely defective wiring, difficulties in electric system operation are probably responsible for a greater number of fires than would first be imagined. Perhaps the development and adoption of more effective practices in equipment grounding systems can effect a marked reduction in fire hazards.

In ac applications it is the total impedance $(R + jX)$ that controls the current division among paralleled paths. In 60 Hz circuits rated 40 A or less, the circuit reactance jX is an insignificant part of the circuit impedance. However, reactance may be a prominent element of the circuit impedance in circuits rated 100–200 A; and reactance is the predominant element of impedance for circuits rated above 200 A (Fig 8). The reactance of an ac circuit is determined mainly by the spacing between outgoing and return conductors, and is only slightly affected by conductor size. Since the circuit reactance is only slightly affected by conductor size, and the circuit resistance is directly affected by conductor size, the ratio of X/R and the relative effect of reactance on circuit impedance increases as the conductor size increases.

NOTE: Increased separation spacing between grounding and phase conductors increases not only the reactance Xg of the grounding conductor but also the zero-sequence reactance X_0 of the phase conductors.

In a dc system the current division among paralleled paths is inversely proportional to resistance. Available grounding conductors having poor current-carrying capability (high resistance) carry relatively little of the total ground-fault current. A surprisingly large number of grounding-conductor design concepts are a carryover from the days of dc power systems.

In 60 Hz ac circuits rated above 40 A it becomes mandatory that the installed adequate-capacity grounding conductor be physically placed so as to present a much lower reactance than the other less capable parallel paths. The manner in which this is achieved is treated in 2.2.

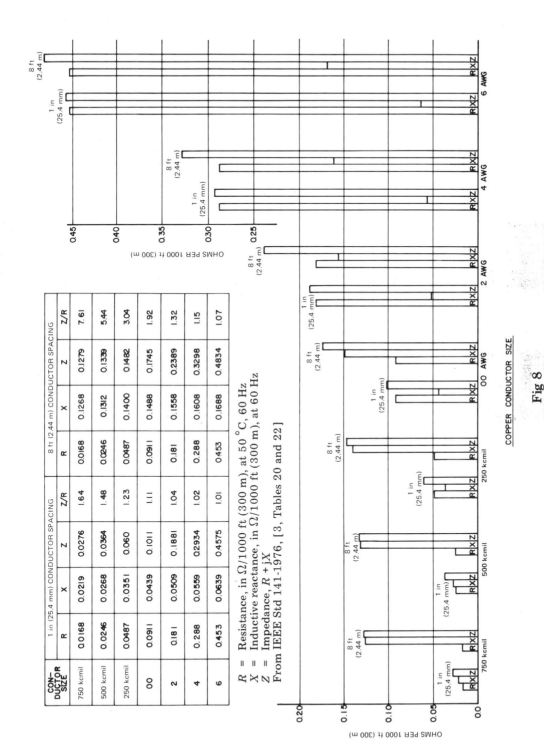

CON-DUCTOR SIZE	1 in (25.4 mm) CONDUCTOR SPACING				8 ft (2.44 m) CONDUCTOR SPACING			
	R	X	Z	Z/R	R	X	Z	Z/R
750 kcmil	0.0168	0.0219	0.0276	1.64	0.0168	0.1268	0.1279	7.61
500 kcmil	0.0246	0.0268	0.0364	1.48	0.0246	0.1312	0.1339	5.44
250 kcmil	0.0487	0.0351	0.060	1.23	0.0487	0.1400	0.1482	3.04
00	0.0911	0.0439	0.1011	1.11	0.0911	0.1488	0.1745	1.92
2	0.181	0.0509	0.1881	1.04	0.181	0.1558	0.2389	1.32
4	0.288	0.0559	0.2934	1.02	0.288	0.1608	0.3298	1.15
6	0.453	0.0639	0.4575	1.01	0.453	0.1688	0.4834	1.07

R = Resistance, in Ω/1000 ft (300 m), at 50 °C, 60 Hz
X = Inductive reactance, in Ω/1000 ft (300 m), at 60 Hz
Z = Impedance, $R + jX$
From IEEE Std 141-1976, [3, Tables 20 and 22]

Fig 8
Variation of R and X with Conductor Size and Spacing

49

One remaining important requirement of the grounding-conductor circuit is that junctions and terminations along the grounding conductor have the short-time current-carrying capability required of the grounding conductor. The failure to provide adequate junctions and terminations is not immediately apparent, because this circuit will not be called upon to demonstrate its capability until the first ground fault occurs on the circuit in question.

2.1.4 Preservation of System Performance. The grounding conductor must return the ground-fault current on a circuit ground fault without introducing enough additional impedance to an extent that would impair the operating performance of the overcurrent protec-

tion system ANSI/NFPA 70-1981 [1], Article 110-10. One might interpret the requirement to mean that a higher than necessary ground circuit impedance would be judged acceptable if the overcurrent protection system were redesigned to display no impairment of its performance properties. It will be found, however, that meeting this requirement is in harmony with achieving other desired goals.

2.2 Fundamental Concepts

2.2.1 A Single Wire as a Grounding Conductor. To help develop an understanding of the behavior pattern of a single wire as a grounding conductor, see Fig 9. (For an expanded treatment of single-line-to-ground fault behavior, see [14].)

Fig 9
Single Wire as Grounding Conductor

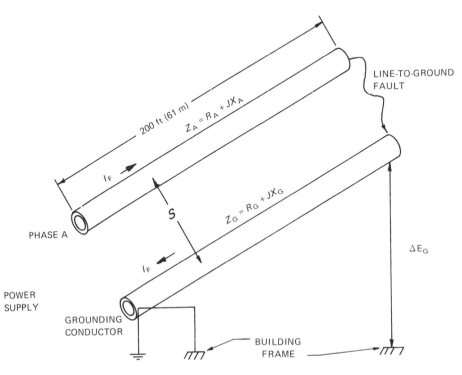

The grounding conductor is considered to be bonded to the supply-system grounded conductor, to the building frame, and to the grounding electrode at the source end of the circuit. For the purpose of examining the properties of the grounding conductor alone, it will be considered to remain free of any other contact with the building frame throughout its length of 200 ft (61 m). Imagine the circuit to be of 350 A capacity, employing 500 kcmil (253.35 mm²) phase conductors and a 4/0 (107.16 mm²) grounding conductor (copper) at 25 °C. It is assumed that the line-to-ground fault current at the outer terminal is 5500 A.

Consideration will be given to three values of spacing between phase and grounding conductors: 2, 8, and 30 in (51, 203, and 762 mm). The 60 Hz impedance values for phase and grounding conductors [in ohms for the 200 ft (61 m) run] are as follows (see IEEE Std 141-1976 [3, Tables 20–23]):

	Spacing (in)	(mm)	R (Ω)	X (Ω)	Z (Ω)
Phase	2	51	0.0045	0.0085	0.0096
conductor A	8	203	0.0045	0.0149	0.0156
	30	762	0.0045	0.0210	0.0215
Grounding	2	51	0.0146	0.0108	0.0182
conductor G	8	203	0.0146	0.0172	0.0226
	30	762	0.0146	0.0233	0.0275

In Fig 9 the $I_F Z_G$ voltage drop along the grounding conductor appears as a *touch* electric shock at the far end of the grounding conductor. At the presumed ground-fault current I_F of 5500 A, the magnitude of shock-voltage exposure for each of the three spacings is the following:

Spacing (in)	(mm)	E_G (V)
2	51	100.1
8	203	124.3
30	762	151.3

The change in spacing also changes the reactance of the phase conductor (relative to the grounding conductor). The corresponding values of the phase-conductor voltage drop (I_F held constant at 5500 A) are the following:

Spacing (in)	(mm)	IZ Drop, Phase A (V)
2	51	52.8
8	203	85.8
30	762	118.3

A change in the location of the grounding conductor changes the value of the reactance in the phase conductor. This fact leads directly to the next important concept. While our impedance diagrams display both resistance and reactance as properties of the conductor, the reactance is in fact a property of the space electromagnetic field which encircles the conductor. For the conductor geometry shown in Fig 9 the magnetic field, which is responsible for the reactive voltage drop, assumes the character shown in Fig 10. Throughout the space between the two conductors [8 in (203 mm) wide and 200 ft (61 m) long] exists a powerful 60 Hz magnetic field with a driving magnetomotive force of 5500 ampere turns. It constitutes a huge electromagnet. That portion of the total magnetic field which encircles the grounding conductor is considered to be associated with the reactance of the grounding conductor, while that which encircles the phase conductor is considered to be associated with the reactance of the phase conductor.

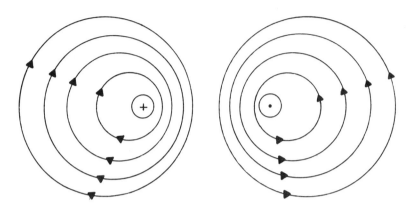

Fig 10
Magnetic Field of Wire as Grounding Conductor

Any loop of conducting material (wire, pipe, messenger cable, steel structure, etc) through which some fractional portion of this magnetic field passes will have induced in it a corresponding fractional part of the 60 Hz reactive voltage drop of the main power circuit loop. There need be no physical contact between the two loops. The mutual coupling is entirely magnetic. If the loop in which the voltage is mutually coupled is closed, then instead of a voltage there will exist a circulating current.

Figure 11 shows a possible loop alongside the grounding conductor (not the most intensive field strength location). With this loop considered to be open at one corner, the generated voltage therein would be 1.65 V for a 2 in (51 mm) grounding-conductor spacing, or 5.61 V for a 30 in (762 mm) spacing. If the loop circuit is closed, the flux linkages through this loop will be reduced to near zero, and the induced current will assume the value that becomes necessary to oppose the entrance of flux linkages.

In the case illustrated, the induced current might very well be of the order of 500 A.

The situation presented by Fig 11 would not be judged to be a dangerous shock-voltage exposure, but the possible arcing and flashing that could occur at a light-pressure contact point closing the loop (open-circuit voltage of 2–5 V with a closed-circuit current of 500 A) could be a very real source of ignition of combustible material (fire) or of flammable gas (explosion). The same size induction loop around a high-capacity outdoor station, where the ground-fault current might be 50 000 A and the spacing between phase and grounding conductors 6 ft (1.83 m), might well display an open-circuit 60 Hz induced voltage of dangerous shock-hazard magnitude. A useful aspect of this effect can be employed to reduce the reactance under trying conditions. By constructing a closed loop with no loose connections, so positioned as to block the passage of flux linkages responsible for an objec-

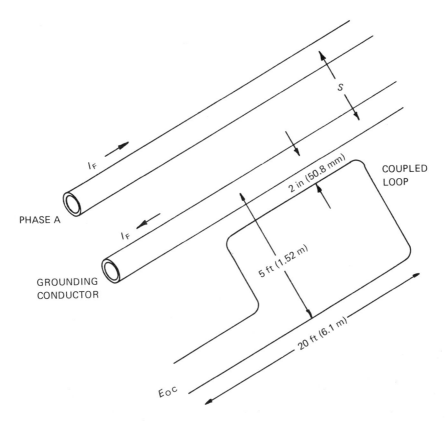

Fig 11
Electromagnetic Induction of Wire as Grounding Conductor

tionable reactance, that reactance can be eliminated. As an example, consider a temporary high-current ac circuit which is required to pass through a heavy wall via embedded steel pipes. The conductors are too large to be pulled through one piece, so each is pulled through an independent pipe cell. Under load, the voltage drop is excessive, and the pipe sleeves become very hot. One verdict could be that the installation is unusable. On the other hand, with the knowledge just developed we can form a short-circuiting loop which will remove the unwanted reactance and eliminate the steel pipe sleeve heating. Locate some bare copper cable (scrap or otherwise) and thread it around the pipe sleeve loop, out through one pipe and back through the other, continuing until the total cross section that has been threaded through each pipe will carry the full load current. Then close this loop on itself by joining the ends of the cable. Close the power switch and proceed. The circuit reactance will be less than if the main conductors had been in air all the way. There will be a small extra resistance accounted for by the circulating current flowing in the short-circuited loop.

As far as the shock-exposure-voltage drop along the grounding conductor is concerned, the key factors are grounding-conductor cross-section area, spacing relative to phase conductors, magnitude of ground-fault current, and circuit length.

In the usual installation the grounding conductor is cross-bonded to the building structure at regular intervals. The first impression is that such cross bonding causes the shock-exposure voltage to disappear. The correct explanation is that the voltage, which was observed to exist on the grounding conductor, has been impressed on the building structure. At the point of bonding, the potential difference has been reduced to zero. At the service equipment a cross-bonding jumper establishes zero potential difference. Therefore the voltage drop along the building structure now equals the voltage drop along the circuit grounding conductor. Perhaps voltage differences have been forced to appear between certain building structural members that are more serious than the original one. The problems of determining what voltage differences will appear between designated points of the building have become considerably more complex. A rational approach to the problem begins with an evaluation of the voltage exposure that would exist with the circuit grounding conductor acting alone. This serves to establish the relative performance quality of the design being studied. It also identifies the maximum voltage difference that could possibly be imparted to the building structure by cross bonding.

Of course a cross-bonding connection from a grounding conductor to the building frame does result in some drop in the voltage magnitude along the grounding conductor. This drop can become sub-stantial with the smaller rated circuits. An analytical approach to a solution of this problem is contained in [14].

2.2.2 Cabling of Conductors. By cabling or lacing together all the conductors of one circuit, the spacing between grounding and phase conductors can be reduced to the point of direct contact of the insulation. With other conditions remaining as indicated in Fig 9 the 60 Hz reactances could be reduced to 0.0053 Ω for the grounding conductor and to 0.005 Ω for the phase conductor. While the grounding-conductor impedance shows little improvement because it is largely resistance limited, the space magnetic field has been substantially reduced, with a corresponding reduction in magnetic coupling to secondary loop circuits.

By distributing the total grounding-conductor cross section among the interstices of a three-conductor cable (one-third-size conductor in each pocket), the effective reactance of the grounding conductor can be further reduced, resulting in a corresponding reduction in the space magnetic field strength.

2.2.3 Enclosing Metal Shell. By forming the metal of the grounding conductor into a tubular shape, within which are run the circuit phase and neutral conductors, a marked improvement in effectiveness is accomplished. The returning ground-fault current distributes itself about the entire enclosing shell in such fashion as to result in the lowest *round-trip* voltage drop (Fig 12). The electrical behavior during a line-to-ground fault is that of a coaxial line. Except for the effects of resistivity in the shell, all electric and magnetic fields are contained inside the shell. The external space magnetic field becomes zero [13].

The customary metal conductor rac-way fits this preferred conductor geom-

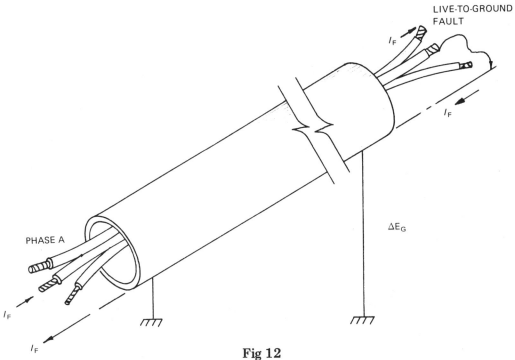

Fig 12
Raceway as Grounding Conductor

etry perfectly. Except for varieties which display too high a value of shell resistance or cannot be adequately joined and terminated, the normal conductor raceway is approved and serves effectively as the circuit grounding conductor. See NEC, ANSI/NFPA 70-1981 [1], Articles 250-91 to 250-99 for approved minimum-size grounding conductors.

Practical varieties of metal conductor raceways and metal sheathing do possess substantial sheath resistance. The flow of ground-fault current will thus produce a voltage gradient along the grounding conductor due to resistive voltage drop. The magnitude of this voltage drop varies widely from one type of enclosure to another. Because of its importance in fixing the magnitude of electric-shock-voltage exposure, a rather extensive

array of tests was conducted to provide specific data, and the results are reported in consolidated form in [14]. A variety of enclosure types were examined, covering a range of phase-conductor sizes from AWG No 12 (3.31 mm^2) to 500 kcmil (253.35 mm^2). The results are presented in terms of voltage drop along the exterior of the raceway per 1000 A of ground-fault current per 100 ft (30.5 m) of circuit length.

Rigid conduit is observed to offer superior performance, principally because of the heavy wall thickness. The striking contrast between steel and aluminum conduit is interesting and offers specific application advantages.

The high magnetic permeability of steel should and does account for a higher line-to-ground fault impedance

[6], [13], [14]. It would at first seem that the voltage drop along the raceway exterior would also be increased, yet the exact opposite is observed. The effect of the magnetic material in the conduit wall is to confine the return current largely to the internal shell of the conduit, penetrating to the exterior surface only as magnetic saturation in the iron occurs.

For the circuit arrangement indicated in Fig 9, the progressive improvement in shock-voltage exposure with different forms of grounding conductors is displayed in the following Table. (The conditions of Fig 9 are maintained, except for grounding conductor size and shape. I_F is held constant at 5500 A. The 30 inch (762 mm) spacing is included only for reference. This spacing is unlikely in most industrial applications.)

Grounding Conductor	Shock-Voltage Exposure EG (V)
4/0 (107.16 mm^2) copper with 30 in (762 mm) spacing	151.3
4/0 (107.16 mm^2) copper with 8 in (203 mm) spacing	124.3
4/0 (107.16 mm^2) copper with 2 in (51 mm) spacing	100.1
Triple ground wires, 4/0 (107.16 mm^2) total in three-conductor cable	70.4

Making the grounding conductor a conduit enclosing the phase conductor, the shock-voltage exposure E_G drops to 6.7 V for rigid aluminum conduit and to 11 V for rigid steel conduit.

The effective performance of an enclosing raceway as a grounding conductor should be used to full advantage in electrical system designs. It is important to avoid the use of raceways having inadequate short-time current-carrying capacity unless supplemented with an adequate additional equipment grounding-conductor run within the raceway. Joints between raceway sections must be good electrical junctions to be supplemented by bonding jumpers.

2.2.4 Circuit Impedance Components. The general expression for the line-to-ground fault current in a three-phase system is

$$I_F = \frac{3E_A}{Z_1 + Z_2 + Z_0 + 3Z_G} \qquad (Eq\ 5)$$

Both positive-sequence (Z_1) and negative-sequence (Z_2) impedance are active only in the outgoing phase conductors since the currents of these two sequences combine to zero at the fault location. The zero-sequence currents I_0, however, are in phase on all phase conductors. Three of the phase conductor currents I_0 must be returned collectively ($3I_0$) over the grounding conductor. Thus the transit of the zero-sequence current involves a voltage drop of I_0Z_0 in transmitting the current out over the phase conductors and a voltage drop of $3I_0Z_G$ in transmitting the current back over the grounding conductor. A correct accounting of impedance for these two terms in the zero-sequence network develops when I_0 is taken out as one factor $[I_0(Z_0 + 3Z_G)]$.

Test results [6], [10], [13], [14] clearly display the fact that the round-trip impedance ($Z_0 + 3Z_G$) is much greater than Z_0, yet the fractional part of the round-trip zero-sequence voltage drop, which appears along the raceway exterior, is but a very small part of $I_0(Z_0 + 3Z_G)$. No easy way to separate Z_0 from $3Z_G$ is available, and in fact no purpose is served in separating them. It is very important to recognize that both items are present and the use of the circuit Z_0 alone would represent a gross error.

As can be seen from [14], the $(Z_0 + 3Z_G)/Z_1$ ratio can be kept low, leading to a low-impedance (Z_G) ground return path. This is obtained by using ground conductors or buses, or both, in conduit runs, cables, busway and equipment, and by repeated bonding of these ground conductors or buses to the building steel, metallic enclosures, and ground.

2.2.5 Electromagnetic Interference Suppression. In developing the fundamental behavior patterns of the various forms of grounding conductors, the ability to suppress the magnitude of the electric and magnetic fields in the space external to the electric power channel by proper design methods was noted.

This knowledge can be employed to make the electric circuit grounding conductor serve to reduce tremendously the *electrical noise* contributed to the space surrounding the electrical run. As might be expected from results so far defined, the enclosing metal raceway is superior to discrete conductors. Steel raceways are very effective in suppressing strong fields. High conductance may be needed to achieve very low noise levels.

The rapidly increasing use of low-energy-level digital data transmission circuits in combination with a fast-growing noise level on power circuit conductors due to time-modulation current choppers, usually SCRs (silicon-controlled rectifiers), for accomplishing heating appliance control, light-circuit dimming, motor-speed control, etc, emphasizes the importance of this electromagnetic interference suppression function [11], [12], [18], [21].

2.2.6 Bonding of Metal Sleeves Enclosing a Grounding Conductor. The behavior pattern of an independent grounding conductor (such as the run to the grounding electrode at the service or the grounding conductor connecting a surge arrestor to an earthing terminal) is very different from that of a power circuit grounding conductor (see Fig 13).

The function in this case is to conduct the one-way current to a grounding (earthing) electrode. The return path of this current is remote from the grounding conductor. In the case of lightning current, the return path may be so remote as to be obscure. There will be an inductive voltage drop along the conductor length due to a changing current ($L \, di/dt$ or $X_L \, I_{ac}$). The larger the conductor diameter, the lower will be the conductor inductance (or reactance). If the member enclosing the conductor is magnetic, the magnetic field encircling the conductor is increased, which correspondingly increases the inductive voltage drop.

In some cases, installation conditions are such as to warrant the application of a metal enclosure over a section of this type of grounding conductor. In all cases where this is done, the conductor and the enclosing protective metal shell should be bonded together at both ends of every integral section of enclosure for the following reasons:

(1) To avoid increased voltage drop if the enclosure is made of magnetic material

(2) To take advantage of the lower voltage drop associated with larger conductor diameter (see [6] for complete details).

2.2.7 Grounding Connections Associated with Steep-Wave-Front Voltage Protection Equipment. The application of surge arresters to transformers (Fig 14)

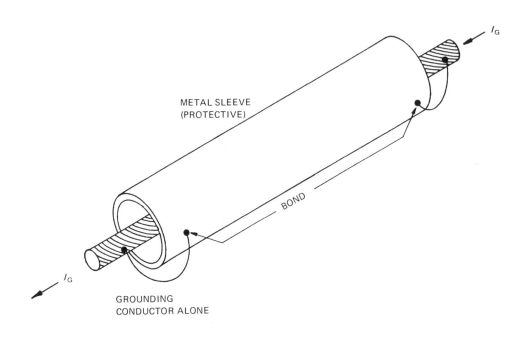

Fig 13
Bonding of Metal Enclosure

and surge protective capacitors and arrestors to rotating machines (Fig 15) illustrate this application of a grounding conductor. The function of the grounding conductor is to provide a conducting path over which the surge current can be diverted around the apparatus being protected, without developing a dangerous voltage magnitude.

In the presence of a changing current (di/dt) there will be an inductive voltage drop developed along the grounding conductor itself, which is additive to the protective device voltage. The amount of this added voltage will be proportional to the conductor length and the spacing from the protected apparatus, and of course to the magnitude of di/dt.

Actual values of di/dt range over wide limits, but a value of 10 kA/μs is repre-

sentative. With such a rate of rise of current, even 1 μH of inductance can be significant.:

$$E = L di$$
$$dt = 10^{-6} \cdot 10\,000 \cdot 10^{6} = 10\,000 \text{ V}$$

NOTE: 1 μH is the equivalent of 0.000377 Ω reactance at 60 Hz.

It would take only a 3 ft (0.91 m) length of 4/0 (107.16 mm^2) conductor spaced 5 ft (1.52 m) away from the transformer in Fig 14 to add 10 000 V to the arrester voltage. Thus grounding-conductor length and spacing become of paramount importance. One can readily visualize that the additive inductive voltage is generated by the total flux linkages which can be developed through the

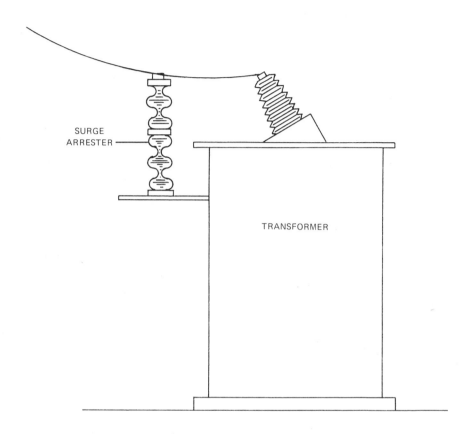

Fig 14
Surge Arrester Location on Transformer

window between the grounding conductor and the protected apparatus.

To take full advantage of the protective properties of the surge arrester in Fig 14, the arrester should be mounted so as to be in direct shunt relationship to the terminal bushings. At lower voltages an arrester-supporting bracket can usually be extended from the base of the bushing. At higher voltages a shelf extending from the tank body at the proper place to minimize the inductive voltage is often used to support the arresters.

The same fundamental reasoning applies to the installation geometry of rotating-machine surge-protective equipment (see Fig 15). A box, shelf, or bracket directly adjacent to the emerging leads from the machine can accomplish the desired objective. The mounting frame should connect directly with the machine frame to minimize the circuit inductance. It is the capacitor element of the protection system that deserves prime attention. If this item is properly connected with short, direct connecting leads, the rate of rise of voltage at the

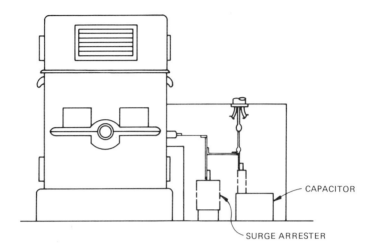

**Fig 15
Surge Protection Equipment on Motor
(Only One Phase Shown for Clarity)**

motor terminal will be quite gentle, requiring perhaps 10 μs to build up to arrester sparkover value. Thus the leads to the arrester can be longer because of the modest rate of rise of voltage. In fact, there can be a benefit from inductance in the arrester circuit, which cushions the abrupt drop in machine-terminal voltage when the arrester sparks over.

2.2.8 Connection to Earth. (See Section 4.) The well-established usage of the terms *ground* and *earth* in our technical literature leads to many misconceptions, since they seemingly are almost alike, yet in fact are not. The electrical system of an aircraft in flight will have a ground bus, grounding conductors, etc. To suggest that *ground* and *earth* can be used interchangeably is obviously in error here. To an electrician working on the tenth floor of a modern steel-structured building, the referenced ground is the building frame, attached metal equipment, and the family of electric-system grounding conductors present at the working area. What might be the potential of earth is of negligible importance to this worker on the tenth floor.

If the worker is transported to the building basement in which the concrete floor slab rests on soil, or to the yard area of an outdoor open-frame substation, earth does become the proper reference ground to which electric-shock-voltage exposure should be referenced.

Thus the proper reference ground to be used in expressing voltage-exposure magnitudes may sometimes be earth, but (outside of the outdoor substation area) most likely will be the electric-circuit metallic grounding conductor. The following paragraphs will show that the potential of earth may be greatly different from that of the electric-circuit grounding conductor. It therefore becomes very important that shock-exposure voltages be expressed relative to the proper reference ground.

All electrical systems, even those installed in airborne vehicles (as at least one Apollo crew can testify), may be faced with circumstances in which sources of electric current are seeking a path to ground. These conditions can do serious damage to electrical equipment or develop dangerous electric-shock-hazard exposure to persons in the area, unless this stray current is diverted to a preplanned path to a ground of adequate capability.

A comprehensive treatment of the behavior of earthing terminals appears in Section 4, in [4], [7], [20], and in IEEE Std 80-1976 [2]. The prime purpose of this discussion is to develop a concept of the potential gradients created in discharging current into earth and the manner in which the equipment grounding problem is influenced thereby.

Earth is inherently a rather poor conductor whose resistivity is around 1 billion times that of copper. An 8 ft (2.44 m) long $\frac{3}{4}$ in (19.05 mm) diameter ground rod driven into earth might very likely represent a 25Ω connection to earth. This resistance may be imagined to be made up of the collective resistance of a series of equal-thickness concentric cylindrical shells of earth. The inner shell will of course represent the largest incremental value of resistance, since the resistance is inversely proportional to the shell diameter. Thus the central small-diameter shells of earth constitute the bulk of the earthing terminal resistance. Half of the 25 Ω resistance value would likely be contained within a 1 ft (0.3 m) diameter cylinder (see Section 4).

For the same reason, half of the voltage drop resulting from current injection into this grounding electrode would appear across the first 0.5 ft (0.15 m) of earth surface radially away from the ground rod. If a current of 1000 A were forced into this grounding electrode, the rod would be forced to rise above mean earth potential by 1000 · 25 or 25 000 V. Half of this voltage (12 500 V) would appear as a voltage drop between the rod and the earth spaced only 0.5 ft (0.15 m) away from the rod. While this current is flowing, a person standing on earth 0.5 ft (0.15 m) away from the ground rod and touching the connecting lead to the electrode would be spanning a potential difference of 12 500 V. A three-dimensional plot of earth surface potential versus distance from the ground rod would create the anthill-shaped figure displayed in Fig 16. The central peak value would be the rod potential (referred to remote earth potential), namely, 25 000 V. Moving away from the rod in any horizontal direction would rapidly reduce the voltage value. The half-voltage contour would be a horizontal circle 1 ft (0.3 m) in diameter encircling the rod.

Imagine a 50 by 50 ft (15.2 by 15.2 m) substation area within which 25 driven rods, each of the type previously described, had been uniformly distributed. Because of the overlapping potential gradient patterns, the composite resistance will not be as low as 25/25 Ω. For the case at hand a 2 Ω value would be typical (see Section 4). Should a line-to-ground fault at this station produce a 10 000 A discharge into the earthing terminal, the resulting voltage contour map would display 25 sharp-pointed potential mounds peaking at 20 000 V. In between would be dish-shaped voltage contours with minimum values ranging from perhaps 2000 to 5000 V, depending on location.

Such a highly variable voltage contour pattern within the *walking* area of the substation would not be accept-

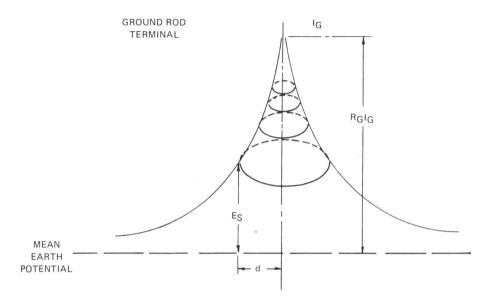

E_S = Earth surface potential
d = Radial distance from rod

Fig 16
Earth Surface Potential Around Ground Rod During Current Flow

able. Additional shallow-buried grounding wires can be employed to elevate the earth surface potential between main electrodes (see IEEE Std 80-1976 [2]. Note particularly the concepts of *step*, *touch* and *transferred* potentials. Additional shallow-buried grounding wires can be employed to *tailor* the voltage contour adjacent to but external to the enclosing fence. Beds of coarse cracked rock, well drained, can contribute to improved electric-shock security. Metal grill mats bonded to the steel framework supporting switch operating handles and located at the "standing" location of switch operators can ensure that the operator's hands and feet are referenced to the same potential.

2.3 Equipment Grounding as Influenced by Type of Use. The principal classes of use may be categorized for our purposes as follows:

(1) Outdoor open-frame substations
(2) Outdoor unit substations
(3) Outdoor portable heavy-duty equipment, such as shovels, draglines, dredges
(4) Interior wiring systems
(5) Interior substations and switching centers

The problems presented to the equipment-grounding-system designer vary quite widely with the different classes of use. The basic objectives remain the same throughout. The equipment grounding system must cope with the current flow (magnitude and duration) which is imposed on it in the course of normal power system operation. This duty is most commonly the result of an insulation failure between an energized conductor and the conductive metallic structure which supports or encloses it. However, the duty may result from an outside injection of current such as a lightning discharge or a falling overhead high-voltage conductor. The equipment grounding system is expected to carry this imposed current without thermal distress and without creating dangerous electric-shock-voltage exposure to persons in the area.

2.4 Outdoor Open-Frame Substations

2.4.1 General. The distributed nature of the typical outdoor open-frame substation (Fig 17) presents some of the most perplexing equipment grounding problems to be found anywhere. It is quite common that various pieces of major apparatus will appear as "island" installations within the substation area. For any single equipment item, the voltage stress imposed on its insulation system will be determined by the voltage difference between its electrical terminals and the frame or metal case which encloses its active parts. The magnitude of electric-shock exposure to an operating or maintenance person within the substation area proper will be a function of the voltage difference between the ground surface on which this person stands and the metal which the person normally touches, such as apparatus frames or substation structure (see IEEE Std 80-1976 [2]). The magnitude of electric-shock-voltage exposure to a person approaching the enclosing fence will depend on the character of the earth surface voltage gradient contours adjacent to the fence on the outside of the substation area.

2.4.2 Design of Avenues for Power-Frequency Ground-Fault Current Flow. This ability to carry the ground-fault current from the point where it enters the station to the point where it is to depart is accomplished by supplementing the inherent metallic substation structure with an array of grounding conductors which interconnect the bases of structural columns and are extended to the island installations of apparatus, routed over appropriate paths [6], [13]. Copper cable is generally used for this purpose, with the conductor size ranging from AWG 2/0 (70.1 mm^2) for small stations, for instance, to perhaps 500 kcmil (253.35 mm^2) for large stations. It is appropriate to seek an effective short-time current capability in the grounding-conductor path, which is no less than 25% of that possessed by the phase conductor with which it is associated. In any case, it should be capable of accepting the line-to-ground short-circuit current (magnitude and duration) permitted to flow by the overcurrent-protection system without thermal distress.

The routing of a grounding conductor should seek to minimize the separation distance between it and the associated phase conductors. In multibay metal-structure construction, the short-circuited loops created by the bonding grounding conductors between column bases may effectively limit the ground-circuit reactance under seemingly wide-spacing conditions.

Grounding conductors sized and routed according to the same rules should be run to those points required for system grounding connections, such as to the neutral terminal of a power trans-

Fig 17
Open-Frame Outdoor Substation Showing Lightning Masts, Surge
Arresters, and Low-Voltage Side Grounding Resistors

former which is to be grounded or to the neutral of a grounding transformer.

Junctions between sections of grounding conductors, if not exposed, should be made, preferably, by thermite welding or brazing (Fig 18). At the exposed junctions and terminations, fittings approved for the purpose should be used.

If overhead-line ground conductors are terminated at towers along the substation outer boundary and the phase conductors continue out across the station plot, perhaps to a point where they drop down to apparatus terminals, an adequately sized grounding conductor should be strung across the area with a vertical down member to the apparatus frame to establish a path for ground current flow that remains reasonably close to the route of the phase conductors.

It is important that the grounding-conductor system extend to and connect with each of the island structures contained within the substation area.

2.4.3 Design of Earthing Connections. The achievement of a prescribed degree of connection to earth will constitute an important design objective. This usually will involve a multiplicity of earthing connections (grounding electrodes) distributed about the substation area. If individual grounding electrodes are not kept sufficiently separated physically, their effectiveness is severely impaired (see Section 4).

One specific design limit may be the maximum allowable voltage excursion on the substation structure (relative to mean earth potential) due to a line-to-ground power-system fault or a lightning discharge. All signal and communication circuits that extend from this station to remote locations must be designed to accommodate this voltage excursion without damage. The allowable voltage excursion on the station structure may be limited by the voltage rating of a power circuit entering the station. Consider, for instance, a station whose main circuits operate at 230 kV, but which contains outgoing circuits operating at 4.16 kV. A voltage excursion on the station ground mat of 25 kV would not be troublesome to the 230 kV system, but would be disastrous to components of the 4.16 kV system. Even the best of available surge arresters on the 4.16 kV circuits would be to no avail. The excess seal-off voltage present would promptly result in their destruction (probably by open circuiting). The allowable maximum voltage excursion on the station ground mat may be set by one of a variety of factors. Once this is set, the design of the station grounding connection systems can proceed.

The effectiveness of reinforcing steel located in below-grade foundation footing as functional grounding electrodes is discussed in [17]. All future station design specifications should call for electrical bonding between the metal tower base plate and the reinforcing bars in buried concrete footings. This can be accomplished readily in most instances via the hold-down J bolts.

If the soil at the substation site tends to be an active electrolyte like cinder fill, the use of dissimilar metals, for instance, copper and steel, as grounding electrodes bonded together in the station grounding conductor network may lead to objectionable electrolytic deterioration of the buried steel members [8]. With today's knowledge, the avoidance of such trouble may be relatively easy. When the soil is active, the required earthing connection may be obtained using only the buried steel members forming an inherent part of the station. Supplementary electrodes that may be needed should be made of steel.

GROUNDING OF INDUSTRIAL AND COMMERCIAL POWER SYSTEMS

Fig 18
Thermal-Weld Junction in Underground Grounding Conductor

If the soil is not active, the intermix of metals such as copper and steel is not troublesome.

Lightning masts extending upward from the top structural members of the station can be effective in intercepting lightning strokes and leading the discharged current to earth without insulation flashover at the station. The avoidance of insulation flashover is aided by higher insulation flashover levels at the station and opposed by more intense lightning strokes. However, an installation which reduces the number of flashover incidents by 60% (far short of perfection) can still be a sound economic investment (see Section 3).

2.4.4 Surge-Voltage Protective Equipment. Surge-voltage protective devices intended to deal effectively with fast-front voltage transients must be connected in a close shunt relationship to the apparatus being protected (see 2.2.7).

The presence of an exposed overhead line running to the station, but terminating at an open switch or open circuit breaker, invites a flashover at the open terminal because of the tendency for a traveling voltage wave to double its voltage upon encountering an open terminal. The possibility of such an event and its consequences should receive deliberate consideration. If found to be likely, and objectionable, this type of flashover can be prevented by the installation of line-type surge arresters directly ahead of the open-circuit point on the circuit or by over-insulation (double normal value of the approaching line) of the terminal end of the line within the confines of the station, ahead of the point of open circuit.

NOTE: This increased withstand voltage also applies to the circuit-opening switching device.

2.4.5 Control of Surface Voltage Gradient. The tendency for steeply rising voltage gradients to appear directly around discrete grounding electrodes results in a very nonuniform ground surface potential in the substation area during a ground-fault incident. This can appear as a dangerous electric-shock-voltage exposure to the persons working in the substation area (see [4], [7], [20] and IEEE Std 80-1976 [2]). It is hardly reasonable to design for a maximum voltage excursion on the station structure low enough to avoid danger. The alternative approach is to employ a mesh grid of relatively small bare conductors located slightly below grade and connected to the station frame. While this will not likely reduce the overall station earthing resistance by very much, it will function (like conducting tape on cable insulation) to bring all parts of the substation surface earth lying above the grid mesh to nearly the same potential as the metal grid (that of the substation metal structure). Only small scallops of lesser voltage magnitude will exist between the crisscross conductors of the grid mesh. The possible magnitude of electric-shock-voltage exposure to maintenance personnel due to earth surface gradients can be reduced to tolerable levels. A surface layer of coarse cracked rock is commonly employed to contribute to reduced contact conductance between the yard surface and the worker's feet.

2.4.6 Voltage Gradients External to but Adjacent to the Boundary Fence. The steepness of the surface voltage contour adjacent to but outside the enclosing fence determines whether a person's approaching the fence and touching it to the limit of their reach could receive a dangerous electric shock. If the fence were allowed to *float*, the adjacent voltage gradient would be substantially reduced. Common practice is to bond the fence to the station ground mat, which will take it up to the full mat potential and create a high surface gradient adjacent to the fence. In defense of the practice of bonding the fence to the station ground mat is the added security afforded should a high-voltage line conductor break and fall on the fence. The bond to the station ground allows the entire station grounding connection to participate in holding down the voltage magnitude of the fence and avoiding ground-fault impedance which might otherwise impede the performance of ground overcurrent relaying. Operating the enclosing fence at station-ground-mat potential also improves the uniformity of surface gradient within the substation area.

An inviting alternative would locate the boundary fence along a specific voltage contour line (or design for a constant voltage contour along the desired route of the fence). This approach might easily result in a 50% reduction in earth surface potentials external to the fence. To avoid the danger of increased voltage exposure from a broken line conductor, suitable guards would be needed to prevent a falling energized line conductor from making physical contact with the fence.

The present trend seems to favor a solid bond between the boundary fence and the station ground mat. Appropriate potential grading shields are buried below grade adjacent to the fence on the outside of the substation area to control the step and touch potential exposure to acceptable values (see [4], [7], [20] and IEEE Std 80-1976 [2]).

It is very important to avoid a metallic extension from the station structure to some point outside the fenced area, which is exposed to contact by persons or animals. Such an extension might take the form of a water pipe, an air pipe, a messenger cable, etc, seemingly having no electrical function. What it does do is convey the potential of the station ground mat to the far end of the metal extension. The earth surface potential drops off fairly rapidly as one moves away from the boundary fence. The 50% voltage contour will be reached in a short distance away from a small station and in a longer separation distance from a large station. Even a fairly large station will display a 50% dropoff in surface potential within 50 ft (15.2 m). Thus it would be entirely possible for a person standing on earth and touching a pipe extension from the station structure only 50 ft (15.2 m) removed from the enclosing fence to be subject to an electric-shock voltage of 50% of the ground-mat voltage of the station. A station ground-mat voltage of 5000 V is not at all unusual for stations operating in the 4.16–33 kV range.

2.5 Outdoor Unit Substations. While the functional objectives remain unchanged, the concentration of apparatus items into a single metal-enclosed package (see Fig 19) greatly simplifies the equipment-grounding-system plan. Even the presence of a single separate line-terminating structure adds little complexity.

The grounding conductor associated with each electric circuit to and from the substation is continued to the substation proper and terminated on the grounding bus provided there. This conductor should be of the prescribed cross section for the capacity of circuit involved, and run with as close physical spacing to the power conductors as feasible.

The problem of avoiding dangerous electric-shock-voltage exposure to per-

IEEE
Std 142-1982

Fig 19
Outdoor Unit Substation

sons in proximity to the enclosing fence, involves the same considerations as in the case of open-frame substations. Within the confines of many industrial plants, the use of artificially reduced levels of ground-fault current (400 A being a common value) so reduces the voltage gradients around the substation that no fenced enclosure is needed. Persons can be permitted to approach and touch the substation enclosure without risk of dangerous electric-shock exposure. Of course the grounding bus and enclosure frame of the substation must be connected to the building grounding system, whether or not a local grounding electrode system is installed.

If the substation structure is exposed to lightning or contains surge arresters, the installation should include an appropriate grounding electrode. The reinforcing bars contained on the below-grade foundation structure will usually provide this function adequately [17].

2.6 Outdoor Installation Serving Heavy Portable Electric Machinery. This problem area usually involving such equipment as power shovels (Figs 20 and 21), drag lines, dredges, and some mine installations represents one of the most difficult in avoiding dangerous electric-shock-voltage exposure. Electric power in quite substantial quantity is delivered to a portable, or movable, utilization apparatus at potentials up to 7500 V.

The mobility of the utilization equipment, and frequently of portable switching centers also, precludes the installation of a predesigned ground mat such as would be employed at a fixed installation. This portable equipment must be designed to permit personnel to approach (and touch) the apparatus structure without risk of dangerous electric shock.

The avoidance of dangerous electric-shock exposure is accomplished by the use of a design concept now widely adopted in this class of industry. The available ground-fault current is greatly reduced (commonly to a 50 or 25 A level). Sensitive fast-operating ground-responsive tripping is employed. A metal grounding conductor of adequate cross section is run from the supply station to each item of portable equipment (utilization and switching alike) and is bonded to each such equipment frame or metal enclosure. No switching devices are installed in the grounding conductor. Circuit plug disconnecting assemblies are arranged to separate all power conductors before the grounding conductor is severed. In many service areas, each power transmission circuit to a portable machine employs an auxiliary device which continuously monitors that continuity of the equipment grounding conductor. Should continuity be lost at any point between the supply substation and the utilization machine, the monitor responds and automatically opens all power conductors of that circuit.

At the supply station it is quite common to ground the portable-machine-system grounding conductor to an independent earthing terminal located some 50 ft (15.2 m) or so outside the substation area so as not to conduct the voltage excursions which may occur on the substation mat to the frames of the portable machines being served. It is important to design the supply substation grounding system so that the magnitude of voltage excursion on its ground mat will not spark over to any of the conductors which are continued to the portable equipment.

2.7 Interior Wiring Systems

2.7.1 General. About the year 1893 a nationwide code of acceptable installation practice for electric power systems within buildings, such as residences, fac-

Fig 20
Heavy-Duty Portable Apparatus — Physical Environment

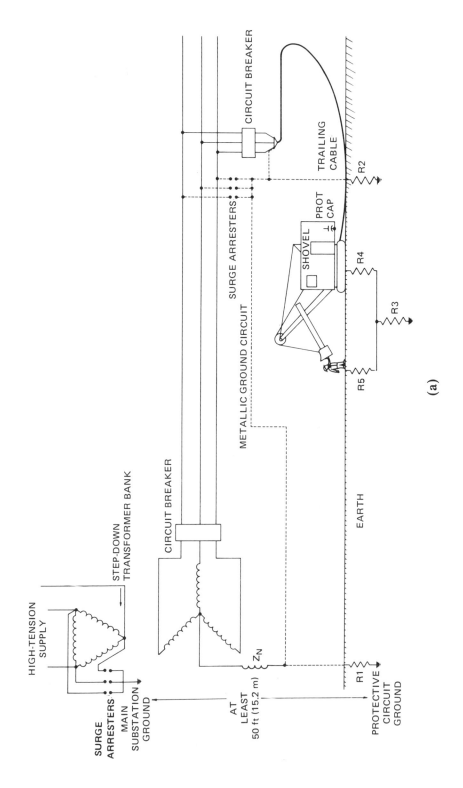

(a)

IEEE
Std 142-1982

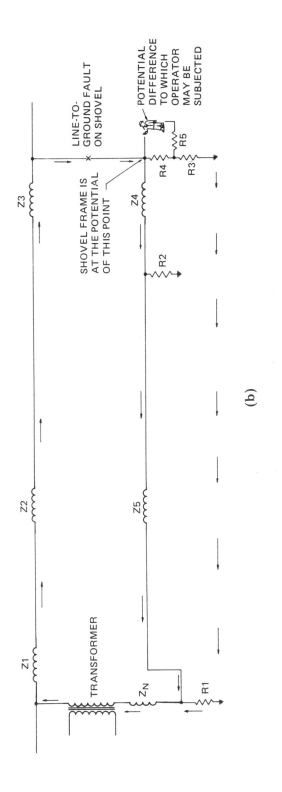

(b)

Fig 21
Heavy-Duty Portable Apparatus —
Elements of Electric-Shock-Hazard Problem

tories, and commercial buildings, was adopted. These rules are documented in ANSI/NFPA 70-1981 [1]. This document is reviewed every three years on the basis of suggestions or criticisms submitted by practicing electrical technicians, and revisions or amendments are made accordingly. ANSI/NFPA 70-1981 [1], Article 250 is devoted to the subject of grounding. All equipment-grounding-system designs for installation within buildings of the types named should recognize and conform to the require-ments contained in the NEC. Basically, the NEC designates minimum acceptable limits, which may be expanded in a more conservative direction as far as the system designer considers appropriate.

2.7.2 Building Service Equipment. The term *service equipment* (see [1, Article 230]) applies to the switching and protective equipment installed where the electric service is considered to enter the building. The required installation practices and protective equipment employed at and downstream of the service equipment are designed to ensure an electric power system which will not create fire or explosion hazards, danger-ous electric-shock-voltage exposure to occupants, or an unfavorable electrical ambient condition within the building. The electric power conductors which deliver power to the establishment, the service-entrance conductors, do not enjoy the quality of protection afforded all circuits extending beyond the service equipment. An electric fault in these conductors may create a severe arcing fault which may persist for an extended interval and represent a dangerous source of fire ignition. In recognition of these facts, NEC Article 230 prescribes a number of requirements intended to minimize the hazards mentioned. The length of service-entrance conductors shall be no longer than necessary. After such conductors penetrate the building exterior wall, they shall promptly terminate in service equipment. They shall not be run within concealed spaces of walls. Special construction requirements are imposed on service-entrance conductors to render them less susceptible to insulation failure. Minimum allowable sizes of service-entrance conductors are prescribed based on predicted load levels and the type of occupancy. More stringent requirements exist for equipment grounding conductors along the service conductor run.

More effective control of voltage stresses in an electric power system can be achieved if one of the power conductors is grounded solidly without intentional impedance inserted. To take advantage of the merits of single-phase one-side-grounded utilization circuit operation also demands a solidly grounded power system conductor. The NEC presently demands grounding of ac systems of 50–1000 V supplying premises wiring and premises wiring systems under any of the following conditions:

(1) Where the system can be so grounded that the maximum voltage to ground on the ungrounded conductors does not exceed 150 V.

(2) Where the system is nominally rated 480Y/277 V, three-phase, four-wire in which the neutral is used as a circuit conductor

(3) Where the system is nominally rated 240/120 V, three-phase, four-wire in which the midpoint of one phase is used as a circuit conductor

(4) Where a service conductor is un-insulated in accordance with Article 230-4

There are four exceptions to the above rules for systems serving furnaces, for isolated systems, and for separately derived systems. For complete details consult the NEC, Article 250-5.

These rules mandate grounded operation of 240/120 V single-phase three-wire, and 208Y/120 V wye-connected three-phase four-wire, 480Y/277 V wye-connected three-phase four-wire and 240/120 V three-phase four-wire systems.

To best preserve the desired security against excessive voltage stresses within the building-interior wiring, the following mandatory rules are imposed on the incoming power supply.

(1) Any secondary ac electric power system that operates with a grounded conductor shall extend the grounded conductor to the grounding junction at each service being supplied, using a conductor size No smaller than prescribed in the NEC Article, 250-94.

(2) In the case of every grounded ac power supply system to these designated buildings, the circuit grounding conductors of all circuits extending into the building shall be brought together at the service equipment, bonded to the service-equipment metal housing, cross bonded to the grounded conductor of the service-entrance conductors, and connected to an effective grounding electrode.

(3) The NEC rules make clear the intent that all interior metal piping systems also be cross bonded to the equipment grounding system near the service equipment.

(4) All single-phase one-side-grounded load circuits shall (on the grounded side) be connected to an insulated grounded power conductor run from the service equipment. This grounded conductor shall remain insulated throughout its entire length downstream of the service equipment (with some exceptions) and be identified by a white or gray surface color. The purpose of the insulated grounded power conductor is to prevent the *IZ* drop created by the returning current on the grounded conductor from being impressed on the building metallic structure.

The intended overall purpose of these grounding rules is to achieve, as nearly as practical, a zero-potential-difference condition between electrical grounding conductors, the frames of electrical equipment, metal raceways which enclose electrical conductors, and the various items of exposed metal building frames and metal piping within the building. To any person within the building this absence of electric-shock-voltage exposure continues unchanged, even though the grounded electric service conductor assumes a substantial voltage deviation from mean earth potential.

The creation of voltage differences between these designated exposed metal parts within the building will be the result of unplanned, unwanted current flow through these conducting members, usually as a result of an insulation failure on an energized power conductor.

2.7.3 Interior Electric Circuits. With every electric power circuit extending from the service equipment into the building interior which supplies electric power to equipment or apparatus that must be grounded, an equipment grounding conductor, sized in accordance with ANSI/NFPA 70-1982 [1], Article 250-95, must be run with the power conductors. In most cases the metal conductor enclosure or cable tray itself can serve as the grounding conductor [see NEC, Article 250-91(b)]. The equipment and apparatus requirement for grounding is accomplished by an electrical bond between the frame (or structure) of such equipment (or apparatus) and the equipment grounding conductor run with that electric circuit. The planned avoidance of any sustained load current flow on grounding conductors maintains the desired zero-potential-difference concept throughout the extent of the equipment-grounding-conductor harness. Only when unplanned, unwanted fault currents flow along these conductors will there be observed voltage differences (with some exceptions).

2.7.4 Special Considerations.

2.7.4.1 General. The selection of a circuit grounding conductor sized in accordance with ANSI/NFPA 70-1981 [1, Table 250-94] will in most cases result in an installation that displays no thermal distress in the grounding conductor if the system is properly designed. However, some special considerations may be required for specific system design patterns and operating conditions that can result in aggravated duty on the grounding conductor. These design changes may include changes in the protective scheme, increasing the grounding-conductor size, or other action to ensure freedom from dangerous thermal stress in the grounding conductor.

2.7.4.2 Mechanical Interrupting Devices. Mechanical interrupting devices such as circuit breakers and interrupter switches require a definite time in which to accomplish current interruption. In the presence of a high-magnitude of available short-circuit current, the $I^2 t$ let-through during the interrupting operation may well exceed the safe withstand value of the selected grounding conductor. The solution may consist of the selection of a larger grounding conductor adequate for the duty, the substitution of a faster-operating switching interrupter, or the combination of high-rated

fast-acting fuses in series with the switching interrupter [16].

2.7.4.3 Single-Pole Interrupters in a Polyphase Circuit. Single-pole interrupters in a polyphase circuit can result in an $I^2 t$ duty on the grounding conductor far greater than the certified short-circuit let-through of a single interrupter (usually a fuse). The sequence of operation may be as described hereafter [15].

The initial event may be a simple single line-to-ground fault on a three-phase four-wire grounded-neutral circuit. A surge of current can be expected to flow between the faulted phase conductor and the grounding conductor at the fault point. The single-phase interrupter in that faulted phase can be expected to respond and interrupt that phase current with an $I^2 t$ let-through no greater than its published limit. Fault-current flow to the grounding conductor has not been interrupted, however. Current flow to the fault can continue via the remaining two phase conductors, crossing over to the faulted phase conductor through the line-to-line connected load apparatus windings and then to the grounding conductor via the same fault path. At the reduced magnitude of fault current, limited by the line-to-line connected load apparatus impedance, the additional $I^2 t$ permitted to flow to the grounding conductor can be many times the published short-circuit $I^2 t$ of one single-pole interrupter. As a consequence, the grounding conductor may be subjected to dangerous thermal distress.

Elevated duty on the grounding conductor can result even though no line-to-line connected load is present. Following the same initial event of a single line-to-ground fault, subsequent action may be as follows. The arc energy released at the fault point will overheat and damage the insulation of the adjacent phase conductors. The insulation deterioration may well progress to the point where a second phase conductor of the circuit faults to ground, to the same grounding conductor. The excursion of fault current involved in operating the second phase-overcurrent device adds to the $I^2 t$ duty imposed on the grounding conductor by the first phase-overcurrent device. During the interrupting function on phase 2, the continued insulation deterioration on the third phase may cause it to also fault to ground in sequence. The resulting current surge to ground through the third phase-overcurrent device again adds to that contributed by the first and second phase-overcurrent devices.

The assured solution to this problem is to employ a more sophisticated protective device which, in response to the initial fault condition, acts immediately to completely interrupt the three-phase circuit. Note that the mandatory installation of ground-fault-responsive tripping at the service equipment (1000 A and greater ratings) assigns added importance to the prompt interruption of ground-fault current on downstream circuits in the interior wiring system (see ANSI/ NFPA 70-1981 [1, Article 230-95]).

2.7.4.4 Multiple Circuit Runs Without Individual Overcurrent Protection. Multiple circuit runs without individual overcurrent protection can also be responsible for dangerous thermal distress in the grounding conductor of one individual circuit if not carefully checked out. The wording of the NEC, ANSI/ NFPA 70-1981 [1, Article 310-4] is often misinterpreted to mean that equal division of current among the paralleled conductors can be assumed, always. Equal division of current can only be assumed for cases in which the origin of the current (either load or fault) is

downstream of the entire paralleled conductor section. If a fault to ground occurs on one of the parallel circuits at a point intermediate between the terminal paralleling junctions, equal division of current among all paralleled conductors is not achieved. In fact, if the fault location be fairly close to the source-end junction, a major fraction of the total current may be found on the conductors of the one faulted circuit.

So many alternate methods of solution exist that it is inappropriate to suggest a particular solution. Effective application of ground-fault-responsive tripping or unbalanced-current relaying offers attractive possibilities. The use of restricted ground-fault current (for instance, 400 A), together with selective fast ground-responsive tripping, as is commonly used on industrial-plant primary power distribution systems, can successfully cope with this problem with modest-size grounded conductors (see Section 1).

2.8 Interior Unit Substations and Switching Centers
2.8.1 Switching Centers. (See Figs 22 and 23.) Switching centers of modern vintage will for the most part consist of an integral factory-designed metal-enclosed equipment. All internal components will be prepositioned to meet the applicable industry standards. Within this structure the requirements for grounding conductors will have been recognized and supposedly provided for. With the knowledge that ground-fault current will seek a path in close physical proximity to the phase conductor that carries this current in the outgoing direction, [5], [13], [14], [19], it is appropriate to make a casual inspection to confirm that these requirements have been properly recognized.

Fig 22
Indoor Unit Substation — Typical Unitized Assembly

Fig 23
Indoor Unit Substation — Back View Showing Use of an
Independent Grounding Conductor with Each Circuit

The field installation problem boils down to a very simple one of assuring the integrity of the grounding conductors. Attention should be given to the proper termination of the grounding conductor associated with each circuit entering the equipment. The grounding conductor shall meet the cross-section requirements of that circuit. The physical routing should meet the objectives previously named. The terminating fittings should meet the requirements of an electrical junction expected to accommodate safely the high-magnitude short-time current flow. The terminating point on the switching structure should reflect the same capability.

One of the most neglected spots is the termination of a metal raceway when it is used as the circuit grounding conductor. Commonly the switching structure contains no metal floor plate. The raceways, typically metal conduits, have been stubbed up through a concrete floor as to terminate within the open floor area inside the boundaries set by the vertical side sheets of the equipment. The following two grounding conductor defects appear quite often:

(1) The metal raceways or cable trays are not recognized as an electrical conductor (the equipment grounding conductor), and no connection is made to the stub end extending into the equipment enclosure.

(2) The grounding lead from the raceway is thought to be needed only as a static drain and connected to the ground bus with only an AWG No 12 (2.05 mm) conductor.

Metal raceways that serve as the circuit grounding conductor and terminate at the side sheets or cover plate of the equipment enclosure should be made up tight with double locknuts and perhaps supplemented with a bonding jumper if the duty is severe. Large conduits, as a part of a high-capacity system, require substantial bonding clamps and cable interconnection to the equipment frame rather than terminating them with locknuts and bushings in a sheet-metal panel which is fastened to the frame with only a few sheet-metal screws or small bolts. Inadequate termination can lead to a burnout at the connection to the sheet-metal panel or the sheet-metal screws, or both, serious damage to the equipment, and danger to personnel.

2.8.2 Transformation Unit Substations. Transformation unit substations present some additional problems. The electrical system derived from the transformer secondary represents a new electrical system with its own equipment-grounding-system problems.

The treatment of all primary circuits entering the structural housing should be designed with the same criteria used for a simple switching structure. An effective grounding conductor running back to the source of primary power is required in case of a circuit fault to ground at any point along the primary circuits or within the enclosure containing the stepdown transformer or the primary-circuit-switching device.

The secondary winding of the stepdown transformer constitutes the point of origin of a new electrical system. It will be to this point that ground-fault currents associated with the radiating secondary circuits return. Hence all secondary-circuit grounding conductors are brought to a common junction point at this source transformer. For grounded-system operation this common junction point is cross bonded to the grounded circuit conductor (on the supply side of any overcurrent device or disconnecting means), to the source transformer frame or other metal enclosures, and to any adjacent metal member of the building structure or piping system if available. Should the secondary system be exposed to external sources of overvoltage surges, such as lightning, a check should be made to ensure the existence of an adequate grounding electrode connected to the central junction of secondary grounding conductors (see, ANSI/NFPA 70-1981 [1, Article 250–261]).

In most cases it will be observed that the primary and secondary grounding-conductor systems become interconnected at the step-down substation. This happens by mere coincidence because the metal enclosure at the substation encloses both energized conductors of the primary system and energized conductors of the secondary system. Functionally, the two grounding-conductor systems are independent of each other. (Had the transformation station consisted of an independent generator belt driven from an electric drive motor, the independence of the two grounding-conductor systems would have been self-evident.)

2.9 Terminal Apparatus. The equipment grounding function at terminal apparatus consists simply of providing an effective bonding connection between the non-electrical metal parts of the terminal apparatus, which either enclose or are adjacent to energized conductors, and the circuit grounding conductor. The sizing and terminating of all such grounding conductors shall observe the same rules already established which depend on the rating and character of the next upstream overcurrent protective device. In many cases where the electrical metal raceway serves as the equipment grounding conductor of the circuit, the bonding connection to the terminal apparatus frame consists simply of a good electrical connection where the metal raceway terminates at the connection box or metal side or roof sheet of the terminal apparatus.

A bonding connection to adjacent building metal structure in the case of fixed equipment is appropriate, although somewhat redundant. The planned grounding conductor is much superior functionally, unless it has become interrupted.

Figure 24 displays the desired grounding-conductor connection arrangement for a variety of power circuit patterns and clearly displays the distinction between the *grounding* and the *grounded* conductors.

2.10 References

[1] ANSI/NFPA 70-1981, National Electrical Code.

[2] IEEE Std 80-1976, Guide for Safety in AC Substation Grounding.

[3] IEEE Std 141-1976, Recommended Practice for Electric Power Distribution for Industrial Plants (IEEE Red Book).

[4] ARMSTRONG, H.R., and SIMPKIN, L.T. Grounding Electrode Potential Gradients from Model Tests. *AIEE Transactions (Power Apparatus and Systems)*, vol 79, Oct 1960, pp 618–623.

[5] BEEMAN, D.L., Ed. *Industrial Power Systems Handbook.* New York: McGraw-Hill, 1955.

[6] BISSON, A.J., and ROCHAU, E.A. Iron Conduit Impedance Effects in Ground Circuit Systems. *AIEE Transactions (Applications and Industry)*, vol 73, July 1954, pp 104–107.

[7] BODLE, D.W. Earth Potential Distribution Associated with Power Grounding Structures. AIEE Conference Paper CP 62-205, 1962.

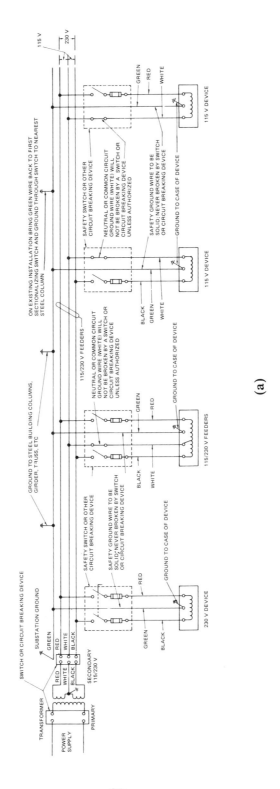

(a)

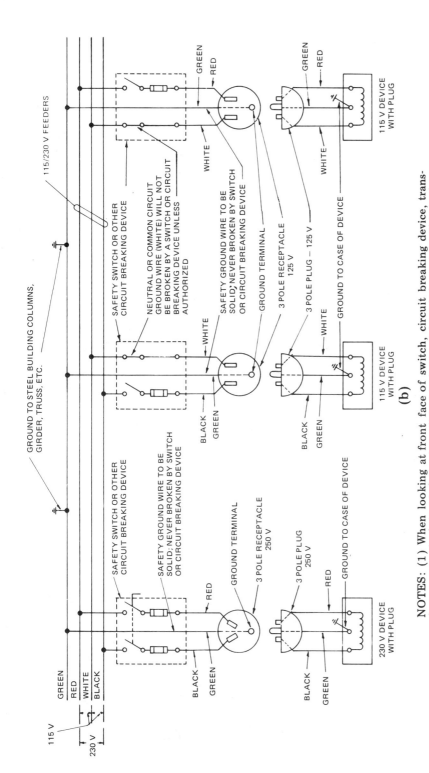

Fig 24
Typical Supply-Conductor Patterns of Power Circuits to
Utilization Apparatus with Emphasis on a Distinction
Between Grounding and Grounded Conductors

NOTES: (1) When looking at front face of switch, circuit breaking device, transformer, etc. the left-side hot wire will be black, the right-side hot wire will be red.
(2) The circuit neutral or common circuit wire (grounded) will be white.
(3) The safety ground wire will be green. (This wire ties on to the case or shell of the device.)
(4) The standard two-pole plug will fit the receptacle.

[8] COLEMAN, W.E., and FROSTICK, H.G. Electrical Grounding and Cathodic Protection at the Fairless Works. *AIEE Transactions (Applications and Industry)*, vol 74, Mar 1955, pp 19-24.

[9] Electric Safety. AIEE Publication S-69, 1969, sec C, bibliography.

[10] GIENGER, J.A., DAVIDSON, O.C., and BRENDELL, R.W. Determination of Ground-Fault Current on Common AC Grounded-Neutral Systems in Standard Steel or Aluminum Conduit. *AIEE Transactions (Applications and Industry)*, vol 79, May 1960, pp 84-90.

[11] GOERS, R.E. Quite—Wiring Zone. *Conference Record of the 1968 Third Annual Meeting of the IEEE Industry and General Applications Group*, pp 249-253 (contains a list of 13 selected references).

[12] Grounding, in *McGraw-Hill Encyclopedia of Science and Technology*. New York: McGraw-Hill, 1970.

[13] KAUFMANN, R.H. Some Fundamentals of Equipment-Grounding Circuit Design. *AIEE Transactions (Applications and Industry)*, vol 73, Nov 1954, pp 227-232.

[14] KAUFMANN, R.H. Let's Be More Specific About Equipment Grounding. *American Power Conference Transactions*, 1962; *General Electric Bulletin GER-1974*.

[15] KAUFMANN, R.H. Application Limitations of Single-Pole Interrupters in Poly-Phase Industrial and Commercial Building Power Systems, *IEEE Transactions (Applications and Industry)*, vol 82, Nov 1963, pp 363-368.

[16] KAUFMAN, R.H. The Magic of I^2t. *IEEE Transactions on Industry and General Applications*, vol IGA-2, Sept/Oct 1966, pp 384-392.

[17] LEE, R.H., and FAGAN, E.J. The Use of Concrete-Enclosed Reinforcing Rods as Grounding Electrodes. *Conference Record of the 1969 Fourth Annual Meeting of the IEEE Industry and General Applications Group*, pp 155-166.

[18] SCHMIDT, W.C., Electrical Noise in Control System Installations. *Conference Record of the 1968 Third Annual Meeting of the IEEE Industry and General Applications Group*, pp 229-238.

[19] SOARES, E.C. *Grounding Electrical Distribution Systems for Safety*. Wayne, NJ: March Publishing Company, 1966.

[20] THAPAR, B., and PURI, K.K. Mesh Potentials in High-Voltage Grounding Grids. *IEEE Transactions on Power Apparatus and Systems*, vol PAS-86, Feb 1967, pp 249-254.

[21] WILLARD, G. The Prevention and Treatment of Noise in Control Signals. *Conference Record of the 1968 Third Annual Meeting of the IEEE Industry and General Applications Group*, pp 239-248.

2.11 Bibliography

BULLARD, W.R. Grounding Principles and Practice—IV: System Grounding. *Electrical Engineering*, vol 64, Apr 1945, pp 145-151.

Code for Protection Against Lightning. U.S. Department of Commerce, National Bureau of Standards, Boulder, CO, Handbook 46.

DALZIEL, C.F. Dangerous Electric Currents, *AIEE Transactions*, vol 65, 1946, pp 579-584 and 1123-1124.

DALZIEL, C.F. Effects of Electric Shock on Man. *IRE Transactions on Medical Electronics*, vol PGME-5, July 1956, pp 44-62.

ELEK, A. Proper Grounding Reduces Hazards. *Electrical World*, Feb 16, 1959, p 78.

HORN, R.S. Ground Your Power Station Safely. *Power Engineering*, Jan 1959, p 85.

JENSEN, C. Grounding Principles and Practice—II: Establishing Grounds. *Electrical Engineering*, vol 64, Feb 1945, pp 68-74.

JOHNSON, A.A. Grounding Principles and Practice—III: Generator-Neutral Grounding Devices. *Electrical Engineering*, vol 64, Mar 1945, pp 92-99.

KAUFMAN, R.H., and PAGE, J.C. Arcing Fault Protection for Low-Voltage Power Distribution Systems—Nature of the Problem. *AIEE Transactions (Power Apparatus and Systems)*, vol 79, June 1960, pp 160-167.

LEE, R.H. Ground Fault Magnitude Determination and Human Safety from Fault-Return Path Impedance. *Conference Record of the 1967 Second Annual Meeting of the IEEE Industry and General Applications Group*, pp 487-498.

LEE, R.H. Impedance of Trays as Fault-Return Conductors. *Conference Record of the 1967 Second Annual Meeting of the IEEE Industry and General Applications Group*, pp 477-485.

MACKNEZIE, W.F. Impedance and Induced Voltage Measurements on Iron Conductors. *AIEE Transactions (Communication and Electronics)*, vol 73, June 1954, pp 577-581.

O'CONNOR, J.J. Industrial Electrical Systems Reliability Takes on Added Meaning. *IEEE Transactions on Industry and General Applications*, vol IGA-4, July/Aug 1968, pp 354-355.

PEACH, N. Protect Low-Voltage Systems from Arcing Fault Damage. *Power Magazine*, Apr 1964.

Power Distribution Systems of Open Pit Mines. General Electric Company, Technical Bulletin GET 2381A.

RUDENBERG, R. Grounding Principles and Practice—I: Fundamental Considerations on Ground Currents. *Electrical Engineering*, vol 64, Jan 1945, pp 1-13.

SHIELDS, F.J. The Problem of Arcing Faults in Low-Voltage Power Distribution Systems. *IEEE Transactions on Industry and General Applications*, vol IGA-3, Jan/Feb 1967, pp 15-25.

3. Static and Lightning Protection Grounding

3.1 Introduction. This section covers static electricity, its generation, proven methods in safeguarding from the hazards of this phenomenon by grounding and other methods, and lightning protection grounding.

A detailed study of static electricity is not made in this section. For more detailed information on this subject, various references are cited (see [17], [18], [22]-[25], [28], [32], [33]).[8] This material will serve as a guide for electrical engineers who are involved with this phenomenon so that they can recognize a hazardous situation and provide suitable safeguards.

Lightning protection grounding is essential for the protection of buildings, transmission lines, and electrical equipment from lightning discharges and surges. A brief description is given of the nature of lightning; the need for protection against lightning for various types of structures, buildings, and equipment; the

requirements for protection; and of practices for protection and grounding. This section does not cover details of calculations in sizing lightning diverters and methods of selecting lightning protective devices. The engineer responsible for lightning protection is advised to use the referenced materials to make an analytical study of this subject.

3.2. Static Grounding

3.2.1 Purpose of Static Grounding. The accumulation of static electricity on equipment, on materials being handled or processed, and on operating personnel introduces a potentially serious hazard in any occupancy where flammable liquids, gases, dusts, or fibers are present.

The discharge of an accumulation of static electricity from an object to ground or to another charged object of different potential can be the cause of a fire or an explosion if it takes place in the presence of readily flammable materials or combustible vapor and air mixtures. Such fires and explosions have caused injury to personnel and loss of

---

[8] The numbers in brackets correspond to those of the references listed in 3.4.

life, as well as millions of dollars of loss in property damage and business interruption.

Protection of human life is the first objective in attempting to control static charges. Besides the danger to lives from explosions or fires that may result from a static spark, there is also the danger that a person, becoming startled when suddenly subjected to a static shock, may fall or accidentally come into contact with some moving equipment. The second aim in eliminating or mitigating static electricity is to prevent losses in the following categories:

(1) Capital investment in buildings and equipment due to fires

(2) Operating costs for storing flammable materials

(3) Overhead and loss of production due to fires

If losses such as those listed can be avoided by proper static control, the expenditure required to secure this protection is good insurance.

An additional need for static control may be for the improvement in manufacturing operations or in product quality. For example, static in grinding operations can prevent grinding to a fine degree. Static in certain textile operations causes fibers to stand on end instead of lying flat, which often affects the quality of the material. Static charges on materials handled by chutes or ducts have been known to cause clogging as a result of materials clinging to the inside of the chutes and ducts. In the printing industry, the control of static electricity is important to prevent damage to the printed images by the attraction of dust particles, and to prevent attraction of the ink to the underside of sheets which may be stacked above them, as well as to avoid possible ignition of vapors from flammable inks and solvents used in the process.

There are many other manufacturing processes or operations where static accumulations are either a fire or an explosion hazard or cause inferior products; for example, in grain elevators; in coating, spreading, and impregnating operations; with conveyor belts and pulleys; dry cleaning; blending and mixing; and filling of tank cars, barges, trucks, aircrafts, or other containers with flammable liquids. Each process or operation may require a different method to safeguard against the hazard. This is achieved by providing means whereby charges may recombine harmlessly before sparking or by preventing accumulation of charges by grounding or bonding, humidification, or ionization.

3.2.2 Fundamental Causes of Static Electricity.

3.2.2.1 Theory of Static Generation. Static electricity is probably the earliest reported manifestation of electricity. The Greeks are on record as having observed this phenomenon in about 600 B.C. They noticed that a piece of amber, when rubbed with another material, had the ability to attract or repel other objects of light weight, but scientific investigation of the phenomenon did not begin until some 23 centuries later.

In a neutral or uncharged body the electrons, which are the negative components of the atom, and the protons, which are the positive components, are present in exactly equal numbers, and these can be separated only by the expenditure of energy, usually in mechanical, thermal, or chemical form. Electrons are free to move from one molecule to another in solid conductive materials. Protons cannot move appreciably unless the atom moves. Only electrons are mobile in solids, whereas both electrons and protons are free to move in gases and liquids.

Static electricity is generated by the movement of electrons which occurs when unlike materials are in contact with each other and are then separated. When two unlike materials are in intimate contact, electrons from one material move across the interface to the surface of the other, and their counterparts (protons) in equal numbers remain on the other body; an attractive force is thus established as equilibrium is achieved. When bodies are separated, electrons produce electrical charges on the objects separated, which shows as an increase in electrical potential between the two surfaces.

If two materials that are good conductors are in contact with each other, and are then separated, the excess electrons in one will return to the other before the separation is complete. But if either or both of them is an insulator and both are not grounded, both will display a charge because some of the excess electrons will be entrapped in one of them when separation occurs, and the insulating body is said to be *charged*. Actually, static charge is due to an excess or a deficiency in electrons, and a surface that has an excess or deficiency of one electron in every 100 000 atoms is very strongly charged. The potential developed due to electrical charges is related to the amount of charge deposited on a body and to the capacitance of this body with respect to its surroundings. The relationship is expressed by the following:

$$V = \frac{Q}{C} \qquad \text{(Eq 6)}$$

where

V = potential, in V
Q = charge, in C
C = capacitance, in F

This potential can continue to grow on an insulating body under the influence of continuous charge generation. At some voltage, the leakage of charge will be equal to the rate at which the charge is being placed on the insulated body, and a stabilized condition will be reached. If the leakage of charge through the insulating body is not rapid enough, a sparking potential will be reached, and sparking will occur before stabilization is reached.

The potential increase on separation could reach several thousand volts, but the charge is relatively immobile, so a spark from an insulated surface will usually not produce ignition.

Static electricity is usually generated by the following:

(1) Pulverized materials passing through chutes or pneumatic conveyors

(2) Belt drives when belts are of nonconductive material

(3) Gas, steam, or air flowing through an opening

(4) Motion that involves changes in the relative position of contacting surfaces, usually of unlike materials, liquid or solid, one or both of which usually is a poor conductor of electricity

(5) The human body in a low-humidity area may accumulate a dangerous static charge of several thousand volts by contact of shoes with floor coverings or by working close to machinery that generates static electricity

3.2.2.2 Conditions Affecting the Production of Static Charges. The possibility of producing electrification (static) and the degree that it will be produced will depend mainly on the following:

(1) Material characteristics
(2) Speed of separation
(3) Area in contact
(4) Effect of motion between substances

(5) Atmospheric conditions

(1) *Material Characteristics.* It has been previously stated that one of the materials or substances must have higher insulating properties than the other to at least some degree to generate a static charge between them. The physical forms may be solids, liquids, or gases. The solids may be in the form of sheeting, rods, etc, or may be broken up into particles that form a dust. The degree of electrostatic charge that may exist between two materials will be proprotional to the difference in their dielectric constants. Also, the positive charge will usually show up on the material having the higher dielectric constant.

(2) *Speed of Separation.* As the speed of separation of two substances is increased, the chance for impounding the charges on the materials also increases, thus increasing the potential differences between them. For example, electrification of aircraft in flight, caused by atmospheric water particles, dry snow, and ice crystals or dust, increases about as the cube of the speed of the aircraft.

(3) *Area in Contact.* The area of the substances in contact has a direct bearing on the degree of electrification because a larger contact area means that more charge may be transferred from one substance to the other, though the charge density may be the same. In other words, the larger body receives or accumulates the larger quantity of charge.

(4) *Effect of Motion Between Substances.* Static electricity has often been called frictional electricity, but actually friction plays little part in the process of electrification, although the rubbing together does increase electrification. This is because in the process of rubbing, more peaks on the surfaces are brought into contact, since surfaces that are smooth and flat to the eye are microscopically rough with peaks and valleys, and the electrons travel only where actual contact occurs. Also heating due to friction eases the transfer of electrons. Similarly liquids sprayed or expelled from a nozzle, particularly if they impinge on a surface, often produce high potential charges.

Liquid materials in a tank may accumulate static charges as a result of deliberate agitation of the liquid, because of tank motion, or while the tank is being filled.

Another example of motion producing alternate contact and separation of materials is the passing of a belt over a pulley, and as previously pointed out, the higher the speed, the more often these alternations occur, and the greater static charge on the belt. The same principle applies to any sheeting passing over rolls, such as in the manufacture and processing of rubber materials, papers, or textiles. Rubber tires [30] rolling over streets and roads produce the same effect, and may account for static charges on automobiles, tank trucks, etc.

(5) *Atmospheric Conditions.* The fact that humidity conditions are related to the production of static is probably well known to everyone because of the personal discomfort experienced in touching a metal object on a dry day after having accumulated a charge by walking across a rug or coming into contact with some other insulating material. This shows clearly the hazard that can exist in an operation that may require controlled low-humidity conditions.

3.2.3 Magnitudes

3.2.3.1 General. The magnitude of static electricity quantities is different than that of power electricity. The potential difference may reach thousands of volts, currents may be less than a millionth of an ampere ($1 \cdot 10^{-6}$ A), and resistances of less than one million ohms (1 MΩ) may cause a short circuit, as far as electrostatics is concerned.

3.2.3.2 Voltages Possible. Voltages that have been observed in a few industries or have been created in tests are shown in Table 1. From Table 2 it can be seen that even voltages of 20 000 V may jump over 1 in (25.4 mm). Such a spark could readily release enough energy to ignite flammable mixtures.

3.2.4 Conditions Required for a Static Charge to Cause Ignition. In order for a static spark to produce ignition in a combustible vapor and air mixture, there must be sufficient energy stored in the charged body. The amount of energy which is stored and available from a capacitive-type discharge can be calculated by the formula

$$E = \frac{1}{2} CV^2 \cdot 10^{-9}$$

(Eq 7)

where

C = capacitance, in pF
V = potential, in V
E = energy, in mJ

The energy necessary for ignition is dependent upon several variables, such as the shape and spacing of the electrodes between which the spark occurs and the composition of the gas mixture, the gas temperature, and the pressure. Tests have shown that 0.25 mJ of stored energy is required to ignite an optimum mixture of saturated hydrocarbon gas and air, but where the potential differences are less than 1500 V and capacitance is less than 222 pF, the resulting sparks are unlikely to cause ignition of such a mixture because the energy developed is less than 0.25 mJ. Acetylene

**Table 1
Range of Static Voltages
Produced by Various Processes**

Type of Equipment	Voltage Range Observed (kV)
Belted drives	60-100
Fabric handling	15- 80
Paper machines	5-100
Tank trucks	up to 25
Belt conveyors (grain)	up to 45

**Table 2
Sparking Distances in Air
for Various Voltages
Between Needle Points***

Voltage (kV)	Distance (in)	(mm)	Voltage (kV)	Distance (in)	(mm)
5	0.255	05.7	60	4.65	118
10	0.470	11.9	70	5.85	149
15	0.725	18.4	80	7.10	180
20	1.000	25.4	90	8.35	212
25	1.300	33.0	100	9.60	244
30	1.625	41.0	110	10.75	273
35	2.000	51.0	120	11.85	301
40	2.450	62.0	130	12.95	329
45	2.950	75.0	140	13.95	354

*Root mean square values, see [20].

gas used in industrial plants for cutting metal is exceptionally flammable. It needs only about 0.02 mJ of spark energy to ignite.

Approximate values of capacitance, in picofarads, of some objects are as follows:

Human being	100–400 pF
Automobile	500 pF
Tank truck (2000 gal)	1000 pF
12 ft (3.6 m) diameter tank with insulated lining	100 000 pF

In order for static electricity to be able to cause ignition, in addition to the requirement of sufficient energy in the spark discharge, it must take place in an ignitable mixture. If the mixture is too lean or too rich, ignition will not occur.

For a complete discussion of the explosive limits of various gas and liquid mixtures, as well as the spark energy required to ignite such mixtures, see [19], [20].

3.2.5 Measurement and Detection of Static Electricity

3.2.5.1 General. Static electricity has different magnitudes of electrical quantities than power electricity, so the techniques and instruments used for the measurement and detection of static electricity are different. Instruments and devices used in measurements and detection are described in the following paragraphs.

3.2.5.2 Electrostatic Voltmeter. As static charges are characterized by high voltage and low energy, instruments that have practically no current drain must be used for voltage measurements. The electrostatic voltmeter is such an instrument, and while it may not have high accuracy, it is sufficiently accurate to measure voltage for quantitative electrostatic analysis. Electrostatic voltmeters are available in several ranges from 100 V to 5000 V. These meters operate on the principle of electrostatic attraction between movable and stationary metal vanes. Practically no current is passed to maintain deflection. Portable models are available. These meters are moderately expensive, not too rugged, fairly sensitive, and do not indicate polarity.

3.2.5.3 Neon Lamp Tester. This device is very inexpensive and quite sensitive. It can be carried in one's pocket, so occasional checks for static electricity can conveniently be made. It will light up feebly when one terminal is grounded or held in the hand and the other makes contact with the charged body that carries a charge potential of 100 V or more. Adjustable series–parallel groupings of neon lamps and small capacitors can be arranged to give approximate quantitative information.

3.2.5.4 Solid-State Electrometer. This instrument may be used to detect the presence of static electricity, but it should have very high input impedance so as to limit current drain. Instruments are available with an input impedance of $10^{15}\,\Omega$.

Electrometers use special field-effect solid-state devices having a very high input resistance and drawing a very low input current. The meter uses batteries, so it must be switched on before entering a charged area and switched off after leaving the area.

3.2.5.5 Electrometer Amplifier. This instrument is generally used for the investigation of static electricity in the field and laboratory. It employs high resistance in the input circuit, and thus has low current drain. It can be used as either a voltmeter, a chargemeter, or a current meter. It is quite sophisticated and expensive and needs experienced operators to use it.

3.2.5.6 Generating Voltmeter. A generating voltmeter, occasionally called a *field mill*, is a device to measure electrical field strength and produces alternating current proportional to the electrical field by electrostatic induction, much as a conventional alternator produces alternating current by electromagnetic induction. This alternating current is electronically amplified, then rectified, and the output is fed to an indicating meter. The generating voltmeter usually consists either of a motor-driven variable capacitor or of linearly vibrating capacitor plates exposed to the electric field. The capacitor serves to *chop* the electric field, creating a periodically varying charge, which results in ac output. A chief drawback to the practical usefulness of the generating voltmeter, as normally built and used, is interpreting the meaning of its indication in a nonsymmetrical geometric environment.

3.2.5.7 Charge Density Meter. This is a variation of the generating voltmeter, which is designed to operate immersed in a charged insulating liquid. The device is usually used in a pipe or with a constant-geometry outer shield. Under such conditions, the signals from this device can be interpreted in terms of the electrical environment in which it is working. Relaxation of space charges in the charge density meter after flow has been stopped provides a measurement of the liquid conductivity under actual conditions in the system at the location of the meter.

3.2.5.8 Static Electricity Detector. This is a commercially available instrument, which detects the presence of static charges and gives both a visual and an audible alarm. It also contains an indicator to indicate the magnitude of the charge. This device is portable or may be installed in a permanent location with an antenna system installed in the operating areas to pick up the signal if static is present. Such an instrument is listed by Underwriters Laboratories Inc for class I, groups A, B, C, and D, and class II, groups E, F, and G hazardous locations. Some instruments may need batteries or line power to operate them. Such instruments must be judiciously handled in hazardous areas to eliminate the possibility of sparks of arcs due to any defect or fault. Test probes used in an area of explosive vapors should be highly insulated to avoid sparks.

3.2.6 Methods of Static Control

3.2.6.1 General. Static electricity generation cannot be prevented, but it can be mitigated or controlled by providing means of recombining separated charges as rapidly as they are produced and before sparking potentials are attained. Methods used are the following:

(1) Grounding and bonding
(2) Humidity control
(3) Ionization
(4) Conductive floors
(5) Conductive footwear and casters
(6) Special precautions
(7) Proper maintenance

These methods may also be used in combination for effective control.

3.2.6.2 Grounding and Bonding. Many static problems can be solved by bonding the various parts of the equipment together and grounding the entire system. Bonding (connecting two or more conductive objects together) minimizes potential differences between conductive objects, thus preventing sparking between two bodies, as shown in Fig 25 and 26.

Grounding minimizes potential differences between objects and the ground, as shown in Fig 27. Bonding and grounding should be done by bare or insulated AWG wire No 6 or No 4 (for mechanical strength), though the current is on the order of microamperes (10^{-6} A). Any ground adequate for power circuits or lightning protection is adequate for protection from static electricity. Even a ground resistance of $1\text{M}\Omega$ is adequate for static grounding. Where grounding or bonding wires are exposed to damage, they should be run in rigid metal conduit or pipe. Equipment or tanks inherently bonded or grounded by their contacts with ground do not need special means of bonding. For moving objects, a grounding brush or wipe of carbon, brass, or spring bronze may be used, as shown in Fig 28.

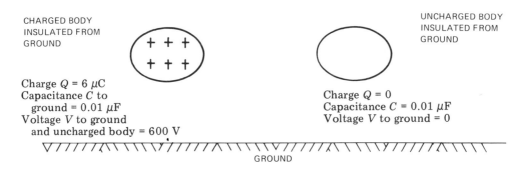

Fig 25
Charged and Uncharged Bodies Insulated from Ground

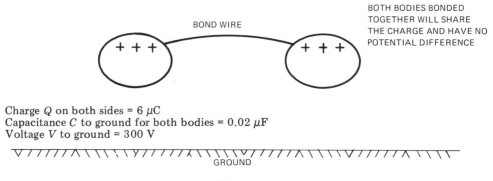

Fig 26
Both Insulated Bodies Share the Same Charge

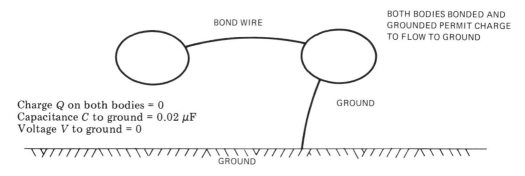

Fig 27
Both Bodies are Grounded and Have no Charge

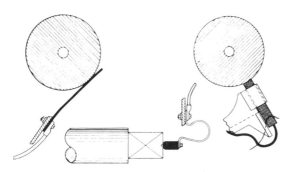

Fig 28*
Methods of Grounding or Metal Rollers or Shafting:
Carbon Brush and Holder, Brass or Carbon Brush, Spring Bronze Brush [32]

Grounding, however, is not a cure for all static problems. For example, if the material being processed is rather bulky and has high dielectric characteristics, a static charge on the upper portion of the material is usually very effectively insulated from ground, and it may result in a spark discharge. In case of processes involving nonconducting material, such as paper, cloth, or rubber, it is not possible to drain off the static electricity charges by ordinary grounding and bonding. Also charges may accumulate on the surface of low-conductivity liquids, such as most refined petroleum products. These charges cannot be removed by bonding or grounding. In such cases, other methods of control, such as ionization or humidification, should be utilized.

3.2.6.3 Humidity Control. Many insulating materials, such as fabric, wood, paper, or concrete, contain a certain amount of moisture in equilibrium with the surrounding air. This moisture or relative humidity controls the surface conductivity of these insulating materials. The higher the humidity, the greater the conductivity. For example, the surface conductivity of plate glass at 50% relative humidity is about 1000 times its conductivity at 20% humidity. At normal humidity (30% or more) an invisible film of water provides an electrical leakage path over most solid insulating bodies and the clothes and shoes of a worker, which drains away static charges as fast as they are generated. When relative humidity is 30% or less, the same materials dry out and become good insulators, and static manifestations become noticeable and may cause fires from static sparks. Where high humidity does not affect the material adversely, this affords one of the best ways of controlling static electricity. Humidifying the whole atmosphere, or localized humidification, especially near the point where static electricity is accumulating, has proved to be a solution where static electricity has resulted in the adhesion or repulsion of sheets of papers, fibers, etc. In some cases, localized humidification by steam ejec-

*(From Data Sheet 5-8, Static Electricity. ©1981 by Factory Mutual Engineering Corporation. Reprinted with permission.)

tion provides satisfactory results without increasing the humidity in the whole area. The minimum value of relative humidity that is required for effective control of static electricity is difficult to determine and will vary with the process and the surrounding conditions. However, it is believed that where the relative humidity is maintained in the range of 60-70% at ordinary indoor temperatures, static accumulations are not likely to reach dangerous proportions. Where the process may be affected adversely by humidity, or where the area may be air conditioned for process control or comfort, and where humidity will not noticeably decrease the resistivity (such as uncontaminated surfaces of most synthetic plastic and the surface of many petroleum liquids), then other methods of static control must be considered.

3.2.6.4 Ionization. In the process of ionization, the air molecules are overstressed; thus electrons are separated from the molecules. The electrons are negatively charged, and the molecules that have lost them become positive in polarity. When a charged object is brought in contact with ionized air, the static charge is dissipated. The charge is either conducted to ground through the ionized air, or the charged object attracts a sufficient number of positively or negatively charged ions from the air to neutralize it. Ionization of air can be obtained by flame, alternating electric fields generated by high voltage ultraviolet light, or radioactivity. This can be achieved by several devices and methods. The most common are static comb or inductive neutralizer, electrical neutralizer, radioactive neutralizer, and open flames.

At static comb or inductive neutralizer is a nonelectrically energized low-cost device. The static comb is a metal bar equipped with a series of sharp needle points or a metal wire surrounded with metallic tinsel and grounded (Fig 29). The ionization of air occurs through the charge concentration on the sharp points of the collector from the electric field owing to the charge on the object. The field is concentrated near the pointed object, and when the charge is above a minimum value, spontaneous ionization of air takes place. When a grounded static comb is placed close to the insulated charged body, ionization of the air at the needle points provides enough conductivity to make some charge leak away from the object. This method is usually employed to reduce the static charge from fabrics, paper, and power belts.

The electrical neutralizer, now available commercially, produces the conductive ionized air by sharply pointed conductors connected to a high-voltage supply. When placed near the moving or stationary charged surfaces, the charges are thereby neutralized at the surfaces or are leaked away to some adjacent grounded conducting body. These neutralizers are powered by the high-voltage secondary of a small step-up transformer (Fig 30).

Electrical neutralizers are used for removing static charges from cotton, wool, silk, or paper in process, manufacturing, or printing, but are not recommended in atmospheres having flammable vapors, gases, etc. Necessary precautions must be taken to protect operating and maintenance personnel from high-voltage circuits.

Radioactive neutralizers ionize the air by emission of alpha particles from radioactive material such as radium or polonium. In the application of these neutralizers, care must be taken to avoid harmful effects of radiation. There use is regu-

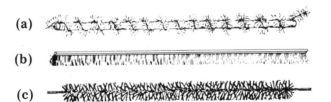

Fig 29*
Static Collectors (a) Tinsel Spirally Wound on Wooden Bar
(b) Crimped Bronze Wire Set in Metal Back
(c) Copper or Bronze Bristles Set in Twisted Wire

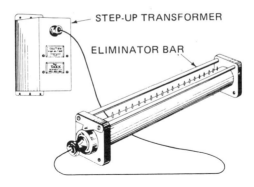

Fig 30*
Electrically Energized Neutralizer

---

*(From Data Sheet 5-8, Static Electricity. ©1981 by Factory Mutual Engineering Corporation.
Reprinted with permission.)

lated by the US Nuclear Regulatory Commission.

Ionization of air can also be obtained by rows of small open flames, which may be used in paper printing presses where nonflammable ink is used.

3.2.6.5 Conductive Floors.

Where extremely hazardous operating conditions exist, such as in the production of some explosives or in processes involving oxygen-enriched flammable vapor or gas mixtures which are susceptible to static ignition, the use of conductive floors or floor coverings may be required to prevent the accumulation of static charge by grounding personnel and conductive objects together, since the human body in a dry location can also accumulate a dangerous static charge. Where such flooring is required, it must be of nonsparking materials, such as conductive rubber, lead, or other conductive compounds.

The resistance of the floor must be less than 1 MΩ when measured between two electrodes placed 3 ft (0.91 m) apart anywhere on the floor. In addition, to protect personnel against electric-shock hazard, the resistance of the floor should be more than 25 000 Ω when measured between an electrode placed at any point on the floor and a ground connection, and between two electrodes placed 3 ft (0.91 m) apart at any point on the floor. Each electrode must weigh 5 lb (2.27 kg) and shall have a dry flat circular contact area 2½ in (64 mm) in diameter. It is recommended that electrical equipment energized from a grounded system not be used or operated by persons standing on the floor. See NFPA 56A-1978 [16] and [32] for more details.

If waxes or other floor preservants are used, they should have conductive qualities. Conductive floors may increase in resistance with age, and therefore should be tested at regular intervals.

3.2.6.6 Conductive Footwear and Casters.

When conductive flooring is used, operators or others entering the area must wear conductive nonsparking footwear. Mobile equipment should make contact with the floor directly or through conductive rubber casters. Their resistance should be checked at regular intervals or before entering the work area.

Shoe testers are available for determining the resistance while the shoes are being worn. Such testers are essentially direct-reading ohmmeters with resistors to limit the short-circuit current to 0.5 mA.

Where conductive floors and shoes are required, the resistance between the wearer and ground must not exceed 1 MΩ, which is the total resistance of the conductive footwear on a person plus the resistance of the floor.

3.2.6.7 Special Precautions.

In addition to the use of conductive floors and shoes, other controls may be considered, such as the following:

(1) Providing wearing apparel with low static producing qualities

(2) Establishing rigid operating procedures

(3) Using conductive rubber mats where conductive flooring is not used throughout an area

Hospital operating rooms utilize most of the preceding techniques because of the extreme hazard of anesthetic agents and the possibility of creating static electricity from nozzles, operators with improper attire, and other causes. The subject of dissipation of static electricity is well covered in ANSI/NFPA 77-1977 [10]. In industrial areas with extremely hazardous conditions, it may be well to consider these recommendations.

3.2.6.8 Proper Maintenance. Like other equipment, static control devices are no better than the maintenance they receive. Therefore it is imperative that regularly scheduled inspections be made to perform the following checks:

(1) Determine if all bonding and ground connections are intact.

(2) Ascertain the resistance of all the equipment to ground. This may be found by the use of commercially available ohmmeters. A resistance of the order of 1 MΩ is usually satisfactory for static mitigation.

(3) Examine static neutralizers to be sure that they are in the correct position, and if of the high-voltage type, that they are energized and the points are clean.

(4) Test belts to see if they have maintained their conducting characteristics.

(5) Take resistance measurements of conductive flooring and footwear (see 3.2.6.5 and 3.2.6.6).

(6) Take instrument readings to determine if static charges are accumulating, either because of the loss of one of the static control devices or because of a change in operating conditions, such as machine speed, the addition of material-handling equipment, or use of new materials which may have different characteristics.

3.2.7 Hazards in Various Facilities and Mechanisms, and Applicable Static Control Methods

3.2.7.1 General. A brief description of the particular hazards met within certain facilities and the methods of static control which are applicable is presented in the following paragraphs. A more complete discussion of many of these methods is given in various references.

3.2.7.2 Aviation Industry. Static charges are developed on aircraft both when they are in flight and when on the ground. The physical contact of the aircraft in flight with airborne particles such as dust, smoke, water particles, dry snow, and ice crystals will generate charges, and charged clouds in the proximity will also induce electrification in the aircraft. On the ground, a static charge can build up in the same manner as it does on any other rubber-tired vehicle when in motion or at rest. In addition, the movement of air and airborne particles over the large metallic surface of the aircraft, even though it is at rest, will also generate static, but of less magnitude.

Fire and explosions can occur during fueling operations because of static discharges if adequate bonding and grounding are not provided. Detailed recommendations for protecting against the hazard of static sparks during fueling operations are described in ANSI/NFPA 407-1980 [13], and the methods of providing suitable grounding facilities for static electricity in aircraft hangars are covered in ANSI/NFPA 409-1979 [14] and ANSI/NFPA 77-1977 [10].

3.2.7.3 Belted Drives. Most power belts and conveyor belts are constructed of insulating materials. These are pressed into contact with pulleys and idlers and generate static electricity at the point where the belt separates from the pulley. The generation of static electricity increases as speed increases or humidity decreases. Static generation will occur with either conducting or nonconducting pulleys. Rubber or leather flat belts running at moderate or high speeds may generate sufficient static electricity to produce sparks. (V belts are not as susceptible to hazardous static generation as flat belts.) Conveyor belts used for the transportation of solid material usually move at low speed, and usually do not produce static electricity. When con-

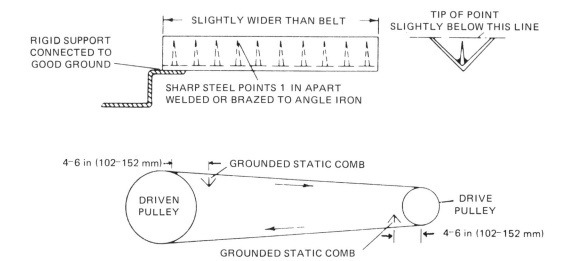

Fig 31*
Details and Location of Static Comb

veyor belts carry heated or dry material, are operated in a heated atmosphere, or move with high velocity, static generation might be significant. In locations where static charges are a real hazard, considerations should be given to direct or gear drives rather than belted drives. If belted drives must be used, the following methods of static control should be used.

(1) *A grounded static collector is installed.* This consists of a grounded piece

of angle iron the width of the belt with metal spikes welded 1 in (25.4 mm) apart at the valley of the angle iron. The spikes do not project above the sides of the angle iron. The comb is installed within about $\frac{1}{4}$ in (6.35 mm) of the belt, 4–6 in (102–152 mm) beyond the point where the belt leaves both the driving and the driven pulleys, as shown in Fig 31. Such devices may sustain mechanical damage, and are seldom used on power equipment. Tinsel bars used to remove static from wide sheet materials can also be used effectively with belts.

(2) *A belt of conductive material is used.* These are available from belt

*(From Data Sheet 5-8, Static Electricity. ©1981 by Factory Mutual Engineering Corporation. Reprinted with permission.)

manufacturers. A very important consideration in applying conductive rubber belts is to ensure that both the drive and the equipment are well grounded.

(3) *Special belt dressings are applied.* This makes the inner surface of the belt conducting enough to leak the charges back to the pulley as fast as they are produced. Such dressings must be renewed frequently to be reliable.

(4) When material transported by conveyor belts is spilled from the end of a belt into a hopper or chute, it may carry a static charge. The belt support and terminal pulleys should be electrically bonded to the hopper.

(5) Metal pulleys are charged with an equal and opposite charge to that carried by the belt, and provisions should be made to transfer this charge to the earth through shaft, bearings, and equipment frame. When equipment frames are conductive, no charge is trapped. When wooden supports are used and are dried out by nearby heat, it is necessary to bond and ground the shaft and bearing to dissipate the trapped charges.

(6) Sometimes the flow of static electricity through the oil film has resulted in sufficient roughening or pitting of the bearing surfaces to adversely affect the bearing life. In such a case it is necessary to bond the shaft to the bearing housing with some form of sliding metal or carbon brush to provide a low-resistance path between the shaft and the bearing housing. Where a bearing incorporates a nylon or other nonconductive bearing material, the shaft should be bonded as described above.

One manufacturer of belts considers that a belt which shows a 10 MΩ resistance when measured on an $8\frac{1}{2}$ in (216 mm) section will have sufficient static properties to make the belt safe throughout its life. Some feel that a

much higher resistance will still permit dissipating static satisfactorily. However, it is desirable to keep the resistance as low as possible to provide a good margin of safety.

One method for testing belts is to place two $\frac{5}{8}$ inch (15.9 mm) in diameter electrodes on the belt $8\frac{1}{2}$ in (216 mm) apart. The electrodes should be moistened before being placed on the belt, and each should be 3 lbf/in^2 (20.7 kN/m^2) pressure applied. The resistance is then measured by means of a standard 500 V megohmmeter.

3.2.7.4 Coal Industry. Many explosions in coal mines and coal preparation plants have been attributed to the accumulation of coal dust and the movement of particles. More than ordinary precautions against the possibility of a static discharge spark, such as good maintenance, proper ventilation, and prevention of dust accumulation, must be taken to avoid such explosions. For a detailed study, refer to ANSI/NFPA 653-1959 [15] and ANSI/NFPA 85F-1978 [12].

3.2.7.5 Flour and Grain Industry. Material movement by means of conveyor belts, elevators, vacuums, blower systems, and other machinery of manufacture can be responsible for charge accumulation and the resulting static discharge. Fine particles of grain dust suspended in the air constitute an excellent explosive. Several explosions of grain elevators due to static sparks have recently been reported. For detailed information, refer to ANSI/NFPA 61B-1973 [7] and to ANSI/NFPA 61C-1973 [8].

Table 3 shows the minimum electrical energy required for the ignition of some dusts when in a cloud or in a layer (see ANSI/NFPA 77-1977 [10]).

101

Table 3
Minimum Electrical Energy for Ignition of Some Dust Clouds and Layers*

Material	Dust Cloud MJ	Dust Layer MJ
Alfalfa	320	—
Allyl alcohol resin	20	80
Aluminum	10	1.6
Aluminum stearate	10	40
Aryl sulfonyl hydrazine	20	160
Aspirin	25	160
Boron	60	—
Cellucotton	60	—
Cellulose acetate	10	—
Cinnamon	40	—
Coal, bituminous	60	560
Cocoa	100	—
Cork	35	—
Cornstarch	30	—
Dimethyl terephthalate	20	—
Dinitro toluamide	15	24
Ferromanganese	80	8
Gilsonite	25	4
Grain	30	—
Hexamethylenetetramine	10	—
Iron	20	7
Magnesium	20	0.24
Manganese	80	3.2
Methyl methacrylate	15	—
Nut shell	50	—
Paraformaldehyde	20	—
Pentaerythritol	10	—
Phenolic resin	10	40
Phthalic anhydride	15	—
Pitch	20	6
Polyethylene	30	—
Polystyrene	15	—
Rice	40	—
Seed (clover)	40	—
Silicon	80	2.4
Soap	60	3840
Soybean	50	40
Stearic acid	25	—
Sugar	30	—
Sulfur	15	1.6
Thorium	5	0.004
Titanium	10	0.008
Uranium	45	0.004
Urea resin	80	—
Vanadium	60	8
Vinyl resin	10	—
Wheat flour	50	—
Wood flour	20	—
Zinc	100	400
Zirconium	5	0.0004

*Data from the US Bureau of Mines.

3.2.7.6 Gas Processing. Gases that are not contaminated are unlikely to generate static electricity. Movement of a gas that is contaminated with metallic oxides, scale particles, or liquid particles can produce electrification.

Liquified petroleum gases behave in the same manner.

Compressed air containing particles of condensed water vapor, liquid carbon dioxide, hydrogen gas containing particles of oxide, and steam, when discharging from an orifice, can each produce static accumulation on the discharge device and the receiving object. This subject is covered in detail in ANSI/NFPA 77-1977 [10], ANSI/NFPA 58-1979 [4], ANSI/NFPA 59-1979 [5], ANSI/NFPA 59A-1979 [6], ANSI/NFPA 50A-1973 [2], and ANSI/NFPA 50B-1973 [3].

3.2.7.7 Paint Industry. The use of flammable solvents in paint-mixing operations represents a potential fire and explosion hazard due to ignition by static sparks which may be generated by the transferal of liquid from open containers, by splash filling of tanks, by belt-driven machinery, and by the workers themselves.

3.2.7.8 Paper and Printing Industries. The movement of the paper itself over the various rolls and the machinery of manufacture tends to cause static voltages.

Where flammable inks and solvents are used in the process, the charge thus produced has caused many fires and an occasional explosion. The static charge is also a source of trouble from the production standpoint. Sheets that become charged have an attraction for other objects which causes difficulty in controlling the sheet, and the web may be torn. Also the printed image may be damaged by the attraction of dust particles and loose paper fibers to the paper.

3.2.7.9 Refining Industry. The fire and explosion hazard due to static ignitions is well known in this industry, and extensive precautions against this hazard are necessary to safeguard lives and property. These are described in detail in [31].

3.2.7.10 Powder Processing. Most powders, when suspended as a dust cloud in air in sufficient concentration, are explosive, and some can be ignited by static sparks. Explosion venting of buildings and the equipment in which the materials are handled or processed may be necessary to minimize the damage if an explosion should occur, despite the usual precautions taken to prevent static accumulations. In the manufacture of explosives, the sensitivity to static ignitions varies with the material being processed. Primary explosives like fulminate of mercury can be detonated by a static spark.

3.2.7.11 Rubber Industry. Rubber cement containing a high percentage of naphtha is used in the manufacture of many rubber products. Static charges generated at many points in the process are a frequent source of ignition of the naphtha vapors. The maintenance of a relative humidity of 50% or more, in addition to bonding and grounding the various parts of the processing equipment and the use of static eliminators, is usually needed for adequate control of static electricity. Operators should also avoid the use of rubber-soled shoes to help avoid accumulating a charge on their bodies. Flammable liquids having low flash points should be handled in closed systems or closed containers as much as possible. When transferring flammable liquids from one open conductive container to another, the con-

tainers should be bonded together to maintain both at the same potential, and grounded to avoid any possibility of spark.

Rubber-coating machines are particularly susceptible to fires caused by the ignition of flammable vapors due to the discharge of static electricity generated by the movement of fabric over rolls and under spreader knives.

3.2.7.12 Textile Industry. The use of automatic cleaning systems for the prompt removal of lint from the atmosphere and from the machinery, in addition to modern air conditioning and precise control of humidity, has greatly reduced the fire hazard from static electricity. An occasional fire in a loom is attributed to static electricity, but grounding the machine frame and bonding all metal parts together and maintaining a relative humidity of 60-70% usually will eliminate the hazard.

3.2.7.13 Hospitals. Mixtures of air and certain anesthetics and the use of oxygen and oxygen-enriched atmospheres introduce fire, explosion, and electrical hazards. Areas where easily ignited anesthetic agents are, such as ethyl ether, cyclopropane, divinyl ether, trifluro ethyl ether, and ethylene are present should be thoroughly protected against the possibility of dangerous accumulations of static electricity which may cause ignition. The principal static safeguards in these areas include the following: conducting floors; use of metal or conductive material for all furnishings in direct contact with the floor; conductive shoes for personnel; prohibition of silk, wool, and synthetic garments in these areas unless used as hosiery or undergarments that are entirely in contact with the skin; maintenance of relative humidity at not less than 50%; and grounding of all exposed non-current-carrying metal parts of electrical equipment such as portable lamps, appliances, fixtures, cabinets, and cases, as required by the National Electrical Code, ANSI/ NFPA 70-1981 [9, Article 501-16]. For more complete coverage of the subject, see NFPA 56A-1978 [16].

In connection with the grounding of electrical equipment in these areas, more than ordinary care is needed for the maintenance of all electrical systems and equipment, because the electric-shock hazard is greatly increased due to the use of conductive shoes by personnel and the installation of conductive floors.

Recent developments indicate that the grounding of non-current-carrying metal enclosures generally required for electrical apparatus used in operating rooms and intensive care units such as electrocardiographs, oscilloscopes, defibrillators, pacemakers, radios, television sets, vapor generators, and electrical cauterizing equipment, may be increasing the shock hazard to patients and personnel in these areas, due to leakage currents over the grounding conductor. Patients in intensive care units may be dangerously exposed. Transient leakage currents of as little as $20 \mu A$ over circuits for monitoring various physiological functions of a patient in an intensive care unit could be fatal where the probes are applied internally. To be safe, circuits should be designed so that leakage currents do not exceed $10 \mu A$, according to some authorities. For more complete coverage of this subject, see ANSI/NFPA 70-1981 [9], Article 517.

3.2.7.14 Dry Cleaning. Dry cleaning is defined as the process of removing dirt, grease, paint, and other stains from wearing apparel, textile fabrics, rugs, etc, by the use of nonaqueous liquids (solvents). The various dry-cleaning methods include the following:

(1) Immersion and agitation in solvent in closed vessels

(2) Brushing or scouring with cleaning solvents

(3) Dual-phase processing

Dry-cleaning systems are divided into the following types:

Type I. Systems employing solvents having a flash point below $100 \,°F$ $(37.8 \,°C)$

Type II. Systems employing solvents having a flash point at or above $100 \,°F$ $(37.8 \,°C)$ and below $140 \,°F$ $(60 \,°C)$

Type IIIA. Systems employing solvents having a flash point at or above $140 \,°F$ $(60 \,°C)$, and below $200 \,°F$ $(93.3 \,°C)$, and complying with the requirements of ANSI/NFPA-32-1979 [1, chap 3]

Type IIIB. Systems employing solvents having a flash point at or above $200 \,°F$ $(93.3 \,°C)$, and complying with the requirements of ANSI/NFPA-32-1979 [1, chap 3]

Type IV. Systems using solvents that will not support combustion or are nonflammable at ordinary temperatures and only moderately flammable at higher temperatures, and complying with the requirements of ANSI/NFPA 32-1979 [1, chap 4]

Type V. Same as type IV, except they comply with the requirements of ANSI/ NFPA 32-1979 [1, chap 5]

At the present time, the use of type I systems is prohibited by ANSI/NFPA 32-1979 [1].

Storage tanks, treatment tanks, purifiers, pumps, piping, washers, extractors, drying tumblers, drying cabinets, combination units, and other similar apparatus should be bonded together. If this equipment is not grounded by virtue of its connection to the electric power service, it should be grounded.

Special consideration should be given to the control of static electricity in the handling of fabrics. When they are transferred from one piece of equipment to another, the two pieces of equipment should be bonded together. Humidification of the area will also help to dissipate a static charge.

Personnel working in these areas and performing dry-cleaning operations can accumulate static charges, and the wearing of footwear that may insulate the person from ground should be avoided. Conductive floors, grounded metal work tables, and conductive footwear are helpful in removing such charges. For more details see ANSI/NFPA 32-1979 [1].

3.2.7.15 Offices. Business machines handling papers and plastic tapes, sheets, or cards often accumulate static charges. These may interfere with the operation of the machine by causing papers to stick together, attracting lint and dust particles, or transmitting minor shocks to the operators. The involuntary reflex action due to such discharges, though otherwise of no hazard, may sometimes result in injury to the personnel. Grounding of all non-current-carrying metal parts of the machine will prevent the accumulation of the charge, but may not cure the operational difficulties which will necessitate the use of humidity or static neutralizers, whichever is most practical.

3.3 Lightning Protection Grounding
3.3.1 Nature of Lightning
3.3.1.1 General. Lightning is the discharging of high-potential cells (usually negative) within clouds to each other or to the earth. These charged cells in clouds normally attract charges of opposite polarity on the surface of (or on high objects on) the earth directly below them. When the cell charge reaches a critical level (when the insulation between cloud and earth breaks down), it develops a stepped ionized path, fre-

quently to the earth, resulting in a high current discharge (stroke) which neutralizes, for the moment, these cloud and earth charges. The discharge current increases from zero to a maximum in, usually, from 1 to 10 μs, then declines to half the peak value in from 20 to 1000 μs. This discharge may be repeated one or more times, over the same path, in rapid succession, resulting from recharging of the original cell by internal cloud discharges from nearby cells. The average peak stroke current is about 20 000 A, although some stroke peak currents are as great as 270 000 A [21].

The point on which the lightning stroke terminates is frequently a point of some elevation, a tree, building, transmission line and its towers, or a similar raised structure. This terminal may be on a metallic structure, which is a good current conductor, or it may be on something that is considered a semiconducting material. These include the following:

(1) Trees with the moist cambium layer under the bark

(2) Wooden structures with wetted surfaces, or moisture residual within the timbers, or internal piping or wiring

(3) Masonry structures with wetted surfaces or moisture tracks down the internal surface

(4) Concrete structures with reinforcing material, possibly with sections not bonded together

These paths are sufficiently conductive to permit the flow of *opposite-polarity* charges upward as the cloud cell approaches, but they are inadequate to permit the severe stroke current to flow without extreme heating or mechanical effects. This is due to high resistance in the path of discharge. Probably the most violent result is the explosive vaporization of any moisture, such as in the cambium layer of trees, or a moisture path in masonry buildings. The bark is "exploded" off the tree, and stone and bricks are expelled by the steam pressure from the structure. At points where reinforcing elements are not interconnected, rupture of the intervening material results. Wood structural members simply explode from vaporization of the contained moisture. Light metal elements in the stroke path may be distorted by the magnetic stresses of the stroke current.

Probably an even greater danger results when flammable materials, such as petroleum or some chemical products, or in particular explosives, are subject to lightning stroke discharges. The temperature at the terminal of the stroke, or at any high-resistance point in the path over which the current flows en route to ground, is likely to ignite these materials.

Even when a stroke does not occur to a particular point, but is completed to a nearby point on earth or another point within the cloud, the discharge of the cloud cell forces the immediate dissipation of the opposite charges on prominent points on the earth. The return to earth of these previously-bound charges, known as an induced-stroke, may be several hundred amperes in magnitude, and can be damaging to sensitive materials, such as flammables and explosives. Low-voltage electrical and instrument devices, too, are subject to damage from this source. Protection from induced strokes is conferred by the same means as for direct strokes.

Lightning can cause damage to structures by direct stroke and to electrical equipment by surges coming in over exposed power lines [34]. Surges may be the result of direct strokes to the line at some distance away, or they may be electrostatically induced voltages. Damage due to direct stroke can be mini-

mized by providing a direct path of low resistance to earth.

3.3.1.2 Need for Protection. Damage to structures and equipment due to the surge effect is a subject in itself, and protection against this type of damage is not within the scope of this section, except as grounding is involved.

It is not possible to positively protect a structure against damage from direct stroke, except by completely enclosing it with metal.

It is, however, rare that protection against lightning is really required for all objects or structures at a given site or installation. A number of factors require consideration in determining the extent to which lightning protection should be provided or whether this protection is really needed:

(1) Personnel hazards

(2) Possible production loss, including overhead and indirect losses

(3) Possible damage, and repair cost

(4) Effect on insurance premiums

(5) Value and nature of structure or its contents

(6) Thunderstorm frequency (isoceraunic map, Figs 32 and 33)

(7) Number and severity of lightning strokes per storm, average

(8) Cost of protection

The above factors are listed in approximate order of importance. In certain situations this order may change. The number of days per year with thunderstorms occurring in a given region is known as the isoceraunic level of that region. The isoceraunic maps of the United States and Canada are shown in Figs 32 and 33. There are, however, local variations, dependent on topography, mineral content, and moisture content, which these maps do not take into account. Also, there are areas where such storms are more intense, and other loca-

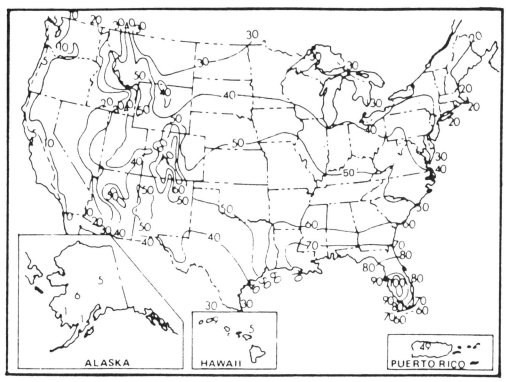

(The highest frequency is encountered in south-central Florida. Since 1894 the recording of thunderstorms has been defined as the local calendar days during which thunder was heard. A day with thunderstorms is so recorded, regardless of the number occurring on that day. The occurrence of lightning without thunder is not recorded as a thunderstorm. Data supplied by Environmental Science Service Administration, US Department of Commerce.)

**Fig 32
Annual Isoceraunic Map of the Continental United States,
Showing Mean Annual Number of Days with Thunderstorms**

tions where there are more storms per year, so Figs 32 and 33 need to be modified to give consideration to these local variations.

Appendix J of ANSI/NFPA 78-1980 [11] contains a *risk assessment guide* which provides guidelines on the need for lightning protection. This appendix is not a part of ANSI/NFPA 78-1980 [11], but was included for information purposes only.

3.3.2 Equipment and Structures to be Considered. Equipment and structures can be separated into five classifications for their need of lightning protection:

(1) The first class, needing very little or no additional protection, includes:

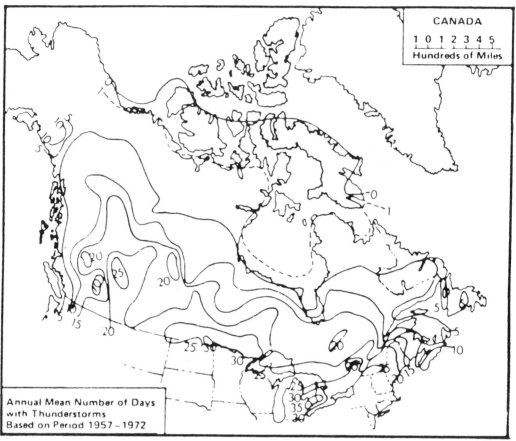

CANADA
1 0 1 2 3 4 5
Hundreds of Miles

Annual Mean Number of Days
with Thunderstorms
Based on Period 1957–1972

(Data based on the period of 1957-1972, Data from Meterological Division, Department of
Transportation, Canada.)

Fig 33
Annual Isoceraunic Map of Canada

(a) All metal structures except tanks or other enclosures of flammable materials

(b) Water tanks, silos, and similar structures, constructed largely of metal

(c) Flagpoles made of conductive material

The only real requirements for these is that they be effectively connected to a suitable grounding electrode.

(2) The second class consists of buildings with conducting surfaces and nonconducting framework, such as metal-roofed and metal-clad buildings. This type requires the addition of down conductors to connect the exterior roof and cladding to suitable grounding electrodes.

(3) The third class consists of metal-framed buildings with nonconducting facings. These need the addition of con-

ducting air terminals suitably located, connected to the frame, and projecting beyond and above the facing, to act as the lightning terminal points, eliminating puncture of the facing.

(4) The fourth class consists of non-metallic structures, either framing or facing. These require extensive protection treatment. Included are:

(a) Buildings of wood, stone, brick, tile, or other nonconducting materials, and without metal reinforcing members.

(b) High stacks and chimneys. Even with reinforcing members, these should have full lightning protection treatment of air terminals, down conductors, and grounding electrodes.

(5) A fifth class consists of items of high risk or loss consequences, which normally receive full lightning protection treatment, including air terminals or diverters, down conductors, and grounding electrodes (see 3.3.3.2). These include:

(a) Buildings of great aesthetic, historical or intrinsic value

(b) Buildings containing readily combustible or explosive materials

(c) Structures containing substances which would be dangerous if released by the effects of a lightning stroke

(d) Tanks and tank farms

(e) Power plants and water pumping stations

(f) Transmission lines

(g) Power stations and substations

Public service facilities such as power plants and pumping stations provide extremely important functions, and thus must always be protected adequately.

3.3.3 Requirements for Good Protection

3.3.3.1 Protection Principles.
Lightning cannot be prevented; it can only be intercepted or diverted to a path which will, if well designed and constructed, not result in damage. Even this means is not positive, providing only 99.5-99.9% protection. Complete protection can be provided only by enclosing the object in a complete metal (or metal mesh) encapsulation. For example, a person in a metal-topped, closed automobile is safe from lightning stroke injury. Still, a 99.5% protection level will reduce the incidence of direct strokes from one stroke per 30 years [normal in the isoceraunic level of 30 for a 100 ft (30 m) square, 30 ft (9.1 m) high structure] to one stroke per 6000 years, while 99.9% protection will reduce the incidence to one stroke per 30 000 years. Protection at 99.9% would decrease the likelihood to one stroke per 30 000 years. Protection at 99.5% is the practical choice. The fundamental theory of lightning protection of structures is to provide means by which a discharge may enter or leave the earth without passing through paths of high resistance. Such a condition is usually met by grounded steel-frame structures. Suitable protection is nearly always provided by the installation of air terminals, down conductors, and grounding electrodes.

In the case of metal-frame buildings, the multiplicity of closed conducting loops within the structure will act to resist the transmission of surge voltages into the interior of the building. A direct lightning stroke to an upper level of such a metal building would lead to a surface curtain of surge-current flow traveling downward toward the ground on the outer ring of vertical conducting columns of the building. Any tendency for a surge current to flow toward the building center is at once blocked by an induced current around the closed metal conducting frame. The inductive voltage drop associated with this vertical surface shell of surge current is associated with a magnetic field encircling the entire building structure. Such a magnetic field encircles every other vertical conducting member within the building, and induces an equal voltage between the top and bottom of each column. Thus there is minimal tendency for any one vertical conducting path up through the building to display a voltage difference to any other internal vertical path. Even though a lightning stroke has caused the top deck of the building to go 250 kV above ground, almost none of this voltage appears as a *difference* voltage between different conducting paths at the top deck of the building.

The surge-voltage protection problem presented by electric circuits and electrical equipment contained entirely within the *shell* of a metal-frame structure due to lightning exposure external to the building is almost nonexistent. A practical knowledge of these behavior patterns can be very useful in getting the needed protection equipment installed at the proper locations.

The protection of electrical equipment and overhead distribution lines from the effects of lightning is not within the scope of this section. The modern techniques used for line protection, however, are very similar to the principles of protection for buildings, tanks, and nonelectrical objects.

Until very recently, criteria used to determine the lightning protection zone depended on the principle of a linear-sided *cone* of protection from high masts or overhead wires. The angle of protection surface from the horizontal varied from 45° for important structures to 30° for those of lesser importance. These angles were to be used without regard to the height above ground. These criteria were found to be inadequate, particularly for objects more than 75 ft high. Actually, very tall objects, such as radio and television towers and very tall buildings, were found to be struck below their tops by stroke paths coming from the side, although the top of the structure was properly protected against the lightning.

Methods recently developed have overcome the shortcomings of the older linear-sided cone systems. These are described in [26], [27], [28].

3.3.3.2 Practices for Direct Protection. Fundamentally, direct lightning protection (lightning protection systems) consists of placing air terminals or diverter elements suitably at the top perimeter of the structure to be protected, and connecting them by adequate down conductors to grounding electrodes (earth). A necessary principle is that the adequate down conductor should not include any high-resistance or high-reactance portions or connections, and should present the least possible impedance to earth. There should be no sharp bends or loops. Steel-framed structures, adequately grounded, meet these requirements with only the provision for terminating the stroke on a metallic air terminal, connected to the frame structure, to avoid the possibility of puncturing any roofing or siding to reach the frame. In the absence of a steel framework, a down conductor providing at least two paths to earth for a stroke to any air terminal is generally adequate.

Air terminals attached to the structure itself are pointed solid rods or pipes, at least 10 in (0.25 m) long to possibly 20 ft (6.1 m) long. Air terminals exceeding 2 ft (0.61 m) in height should be supported at a point not less than one half their height. These air terminals are separated by distances determined through use of the *critical radius* described in [26], [27], [29], so that the structure surface will not protrude through or beyond the surface of protection. On building edges, 10 in (0.25 m) terminals should not be separated more than 20 ft (6.1 m), and 2 ft (0.61 m) terminals should not be separated more than 25 ft (7.6 m). Within the periphery, 50 ft (15.2 m) spacing will suffice. Refer to ANSI/NFPA 78-1980 [11].

All air terminals should be connected by down conductors and should form a two-way path from each air terminal to make connection to the grounding electrode (voltages double at an open circuit or end, in a lightning down conductor). Bend radii should be as long as possible, since sharp bends increase the reactance of the conductor. Reactance is much more important than resistance, because of the very high frequency of the surge front. At least two down conductors should be provided on all structures, except that only one down conductor is needed for masts, spires, and flagpoles.

The location of down conductors will depend on the location of the air terminals, the size of the structure being protected, the most direct routing, the security against damage or displacement, the location of metallic bodies, water pipes, the grounding electrode, and the ground conditions. If the structure has metallic columns, these columns will act as down conductors. The air terminals must be interconnected by conductors to make connection with the columns. The average distance between down conductors should not exceed 100 ft (30 m). Irregularly shaped structures may require extra down conductors. Down conductors passing through runways, driveways, playgrounds, public walks, etc, should be guarded to prevent their damage or displacement. If a down conductor is run through ferrous metal tube or pipe, the conductor must be bonded at both ends of the tube or pipe.

Every down conductor must be connected, at its base, to an earthing or grounding electrode. This electrode needs to be not less than 2 ft (0.61 m) away from the base of the building and should extend below the building foundation if possible. The length of the grounding conductor is highly important. A horizontal run of, say, 50 ft (15.2 m) to a better electrode (such as a water pipe) is much less effective than a connection to a driven rod alongside the structure itself. Electrodes should make contact with the earth from the surface downward to avoid flashing at the surface. Earth connections should be made at uniform intervals about the structure, avoiding as much as possible the grouping of connections on one side. Properly made connections to earth are an essential feature of a lightning-rod system for the protection of buildings (see Section 4).

Naturally, the greater the number of down conductors and grounding electrodes, the lower will be the voltage developed within the protection system, and the better it will perform. This is one of the great advantages of the steel-framed building. It has as many down conductors as it has columns, or one about every 15 ft (4.57 m). Also, at the bottom of each column it has a footing, which is a very effective electrode, even if anchor bolts and reinforcing bar are not interconnected (see Section 4).

Interior metal parts of a non-metal-framed building which are within 6 ft (1.83 m) of a down conductor need to be connected to that down conductor. Otherwise they may sustain side flashes from it, which occur because of voltage drop in the lower portion of that down conductor and electrode. The same is true for the juxtaposition of interior metal parts and exterior metal roofing or sheathing. Exterior emergency ladders should also be bonded to the nearest down conductor. On a flat-top building protected by air terminals, all metallic parts and equipment projecting higher than the air terminals, such as air-conditioning and heating equipment, should be bonded to the lightning protection system. Metal less than $\frac{3}{16}$ in (4.76 mm) thick should have an air terminal mounted on top.

For high-rise buildings and towers, an equalizing horizontal bonding loop should be installed at approximately every 100 ft (30 m). This bonding loop should be connected at every down conductor to equalize the voltage differences between down conductors. If this is not done, during severe lightning strokes a voltage will appear between down-conductors as the surge impedance of each down conductor is different, causing high-voltage gradients between these down conductors. These equalizing loops become more important if the structure area is small since in this case there are fewer down conductors to carry the total stroke current.

3.3.4 Practices for Lightning Protection.

3.3.4.1 General. Buildings and structures involving hazardous liquids, gases, or explosives require additional protection. In these it is highly desirable to keep the stroke current away from the structure, not even utilizing its metal skin or framework as a down conductor. For such cases, including tanks, tank farms, and explosive manufacture and storage, a separate diverter protection system is employed.

The diverter element consists of one or more masts, or one or more elevated wires (between masts or poles), meeting the requirements of lightning protection [26], [27], [29]. The masts or poles are normally at least 10 ft (3 m) from any part of the structure to be protected. Similarly, elevated wires above the structure must remain not less than 10 ft (3 m) above the structure (Fig 34). Metal masts may act as grounding conductors. Wood poles should have an air terminal securely mounted to the top of the pole, and a copper or copperweld conductor along the pole should be provided as grounding conductor. The guy wires for an elevated wire span can be designed to serve as grounding conductors. As with all other types of grounding conductors, suitable earthing electrodes are necessary.

3.3.4.2 Tanks and Tank Farms. In some places it is not considered necessary to protect tanks containing flammable liquids or gases from lightning, provided the base of the tanks are adequately grounded. Direct strokes are permitted to the tank top or walls, and as long as the steel is $\frac{3}{16}$ in (4.76 mm) or more in thickness, there is little danger of a stroke puncturing it. Steel tanks with steel roofs and floating metal roofs are generally considered to be self-protecting. Tanks with nonmetallic roofs are not self-protecting and should usually be protected with air terminals, conducting masts, or elevated ground wires. In all cases, joints and piping connections should be electrically continuous, and all vapor or gas openings closed or flameproof. The possibility of a direct stroke to the vicinity of a vent or leak is taken care of by an air terminal of suitable length [26], [27], [29].

3.3.4.3 Non-Conducting Heavy-Duty Stacks. For heavy-duty stacks, including those in petroleum and chemical plants, air terminals, connected to a loop conductor around the top of the stack,

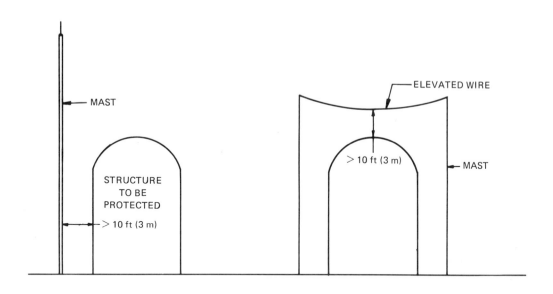

Fig 34
Lightning Protection for Structures Containing Hazardous Materials

and at least two down conductors to grounding electrodes at the base of the stack are required (Fig 35). Air terminals should be made of solid copper or stainless steel and should be uniformly distributed around the top of cylindrical stacks at intervals not exceeding 8 ft (2.44 m). On square or rectangular stacks, air terminals should be located not more than 2 ft (0.61 m) from the corners and should be spaced not more than 8 ft (2.44 m) apart around the perimeter. Where the stack gas is nonflammable, the length of the terminals may be as little as 18 in (0.46 m). Where ventilating stacks emit explosive gas or dust, the length of the air terminals should be not less than 5 ft (1.52 m). Where the gas or dust is explosive and under forced

draft, the length should be not less than 15 ft (4.57 m). In the latter case, tilting the terminals outward at 30° from the vertical is desirable.

Where the effluent is corrosive, as in flue gas, $\frac{1}{16}$ in (1.6 mm) thick lead coating on the air terminals is required. The loop is also kept below the top of the stack.

3.3.4.4 Steeples. Steeples are similar to stacks except that they normally are sharp peaked and thus require only one air terminal. This should project far enough above the top ornamentation to meet the requirements of lightning protection. Otherwise multiple air terminals or a multipointed terminal should be used to provide equivalent protection.

Steeples are frequently framed with

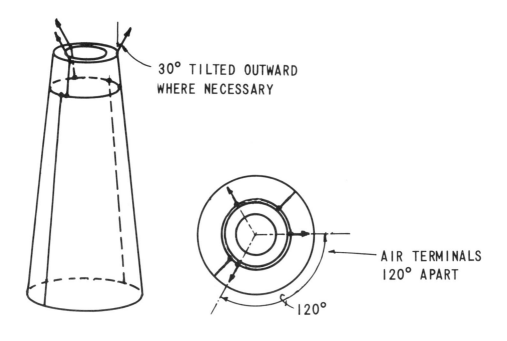

30° TILTED OUTWARD
WHERE NECESSARY

AIR TERMINALS
120° APART

120°

Fig 35
Lightning Protection for Stacks

wood, not metal, so adequate down conductors are a basic requirement.

3.3.4.5 High Masts. Equipment on the sides of very high masts, such as television or FM antennas, can be protected from direct stroke damage by the addition of lateral spikes or *thorns* projecting outward from the sides of the mast. At heights above the critical radius of 100 or 200 ft (30 or 60 m) [26], [27], [29], spikes in a horizontal or near-horizontal position, suitably spaced as described in [26], [27], [29], will cause strokes coming from the side to terminate on the spikes rather than on the mast itself. This will greatly reduce the possibility of damage to electrically fragile components by the termination of the lightning stroke arc. The number of spikes around the mast (three, four, five, or six), the length of the spikes, and their vertical spacing along the mast need to be determined for optimum economics, and according to the principles of lightning protection. Where masts are installed on top of a building, the bottom of the mast structure must be bonded at least at two points with the building grounding network.

3.3.4.6 Power Stations and Substations. While transmission-line protection against lightning is an inherent part of its design and is well documented, the protection of stations and substations has received little attention. If anything, the old 30°–45° cone of protection philosophy for building protection has been applied to these important items as well.

Stations and substations require protection from direct strokes, obtainable using the circular-sided protection zone guidance set forth in [26], [27], [29]. Masts or overhead wires, or both, may be used. The grounding of these to the usually very adequate grounding network of the station or substation is, of course, necessary.

Protection of the attached overhead lines by means of an overhead grounded conductor or diverter (static wire) for 2000 ft (610 m) away from the station or substation is recommended. This will preclude direct strokes on this section of the line, and reduce the duty on the station surge arresters. The spacing of this overhead grounded conductor or diverter and its down conductors from the phase conductors must be not less than the basic impulse insulation level of the lightning protection system. Otherwise side flashes to the phase conductors will occur, causing unnecessary outages. Generally unless the lines are 66 kV or higher, it is not practical to install these overhead grounded conductors above them.

However, overhead grounded conductors may be desirable on some power lines below 66 kV, depending on past experience with such lines operating in high isoceraunic levels.

Lightning protection of power stations and substations includes the protection of station equipment by means of surge arresters [34]. These arresters should be mounted on, or closely connected to, the frames of the principal equipment which they are protecting, especially transformers (Fig 36). They may also be mounted on the steel framework of the station or substation where all components are closely interconnected by means of the grounding grid. Substation grounding network resistance must not exceed 5 Ω; for large stations, lower values are desirable.

The surge-arrester grounding conductor should be connected into the common station ground bus. As with lightning down conductors, the grounding conductor for surge arresters must be as short and straight as possible. The National Electrical Code, ANSI/NFPA 70-1981 [9, Article 280] requires that it be not less than AWG No 6 (4.11 mm), but larger sizes may be desirable with larger systems, based on the magnitude of the power follow current.

3.4 References

[1] ANSI/NFPA 32-1979, Drycleaning Plants.

[2] ANSI/NFPA 50A-1973, Gaseous Hydrogen Systems at Consumer Sites.

[3] ANSI/NFPA 50B-1973, Liquefied Hydrogen Systems.

[4] ANSI/NFPA 58-1979, Storage and Handling of Liquefied Petroleum Gases.

[5] ANSI/NFPA 59-1979, Liquefied Petroleum Gases at Utility Gas Plants.

[6] ANSI/NFPA 59A-1979, Storage and Handling of Liquefied Natural Gas.

[7] ANSI/NFPA 61B-1973, Prevention of Fire and Dust Explosions in Grain Elevators and Bulk Grain Handling Facilities.

[8] ANSI/NFPA 61C-1973, Prevention of Fire and Dust Explosions in Feed Mills.

[9] ANSI/NFPA 70-1981, National Electrical Code.

[10] ANSI/NFPA 77-1977, Static Electricity.

Fig 36
Typical Method of Grounding Surge Arrester

[11] ANSI/NFPA 78-1980, Lightning Protection Code.

[12] ANSI/NFPA 85F-1978, Standard for the Installation and Operation of Pulverized-Fuel Systems.

[13] ANSI/NFPA 407-1980, Aircraft Fuel Servicing.

[14] ANSI/NFPA 409-1979, Aircraft Hangars.

[15] ANSI/NFPA 653-1959, Prevention of Dust Explosions in Coal Preparation Plants.

[16] NFPA 56A-1978, Inhalation Anesthetic Code.[9]

[17] BEACH, R. Electrostatic Hazards and Their Control.

[18] BEACH, R. Grounding Principles and Practice—V: Static Electricity in Industry. *Electrical Engineering*, vol 64, May 1945, pp 184–194.

[19] BEACH, R. Industrial Fires and Explosions from Electrostatic Origin. *Mechanical Engineering*, Apr 1953.

[20] COLLINS, A.F., and DUFFIN, D.J. *Radio Amateurs Handbook*. New York: Crowell, 1949.

[21] DAVIS, N.H. Lightning Protection Systems. *NFPA Fire Protection Handbook*, 15th ed, chap 12.

[22] EICHEL, F.G. Electrostatics. *Chemical Engineering*. Mar 13, 1967.

[23] GALLY, S.K. Elements of Static Electricity. *Gas*, Mar 1949, pp 42–46.

[24] HARPER, W. R. *Contact and Frictional Electrification*. New York: Oxford University Press, 1967.

[25] KLINKENBERG, A., and VAN DER MINNE, J.L. *Electrostatics in the Petroleum Industry*. New York: Elsevier Publishing Company, 1958.

[26] LEE, R.H. Protection Zone for Buildings Against Lightning Strokes Using Transmission Line Protection Practice. *IEEE Transactions on Industry Applications*, vol IA-14, Nov/Dec 1978.

[27] LEE, R.H. Lightning Protection of Buildings. *IEEE Transaction on Industry Applications*, vol IA-15, May/June 1979.

[28] LOEB, L.B. The Basic Mechanisms of Static Electrification. *Science*, Dec 7, 1945, pp 573–576.

[29] OFFERMANN, P.F. Lightning Protection of Structures. *Conference Record of the 1969 Fourth Annual Meeting of the IEEE Industry and General Applications Group*, 69C5-IGA.

[30] PEARSON, J.M. Protection Against Static Electricity. *Automotive Transactions*, vol 21, 1940.

[31] API-RP-2003 1982. Recommended Practice for Protection Against Ignitions Arising out of Static. Lightning and Stray Currents.[10]

[32] Static Electricity, in *Handbook of Industrial Loss Prevention*. Factory Mutual Engineering Corporation, 1968, chap 30.

[33] Static Electricity. Circular C-438. National Bureau of Standards, Boulder, CO, United States Government Printing Office, Washington, DC.

[34] WALSH, G.W. A Review of Lightning Protection and Grounding Practices. *IEEE Transactions on Industry Applications*, vol IA-9, Mar/Apr 1973.

---

[9] This document is available from the National Fire Protection Association Publication Sales Division, Batterymarch Park, Quincy, MA 02269.

[10] American Petroleum Institute, 2101 L Street N W Washington, DC 20032

3.5 Bibliography

BEACH, R. Mechanical Electrostatic Neutralizer Discharge and Safety Characteristics. *Mechanical Engineering*, vol 71, pp 329–334.

HEDLUND, C.F. Lightning Protection for Buildings. *IEEE Transactions on Industry and General Applications*, vol IGA-3, Jan/Feb 1967, pp 26–30.

HUGHES, J.F., and BRIGHT, A.W. Electrostatic Hazards Associated with Power Handling in Silo Installations. *IEEE Transactions on Industry Applications*, vol IA-15, Jan/Feb 1979.

LEWIS, B., and VON ELBE, G. *Combustion, Flames and Explosions*. New York: Academic Press, 1951.

4. Connection to Earth

4.1 Resistance to Earth

4.1.1 Nature of Grounding Resistance.
The grounding resistance of an electrode is made up of:

(1) Resistance of the (metal) electrode

(2) Contact resistance between the electrode and the soil

(3) Resistance of the soil, from the electrode surface outward, in the geometry set up for the flow of current outward from the electrode to infinite earth

The first two resistances are very small fractions of an ohm and can be neglected for all practical purposes. So the third element is the one to be discussed here.

Around a rod this resistance is the sum of the series resistances of virtual shells of earth, located progressively outward from the rod. The shell nearest the rod has the smallest circumferential area or cross section, so it has the highest resistance. Successive shells outside this one have progressively larger areas, and thus progressively lower resistances. As the radius outward from the rod increases to about 20 ft (6 m), the incremental resistance per unit of radius decreases effectively to nearly zero.

To help visualize this, Fig 37 shows a typical 10 ft (3 m) by $\frac{5}{8}$ in (16 mm) ground rod in soil. The path of ground current outward from the rod surface consists of successive cylindrical and hemispherical shells. As the distance from the rod increases, so do the cross-sectional areas of the individual shells. As their areas increase, their individual series resistances decrease inversely with the area. Table 4 shows the result of carrying out this calculation based on the distance of 25 ft (7.62 m) representing 100% of the total earth resistance. The table shows that in the first 0.1 ft (0.03 m) away from the rod surface, 25% of the total resistance is incurred. In the first 0.5 ft (0.15 m) and 1.0 ft (0.3 m), 52 and 68%, respectively, of the total resistance is incurred.

The Dwight formula for single rods, shown in Table 8, would place this re-

119

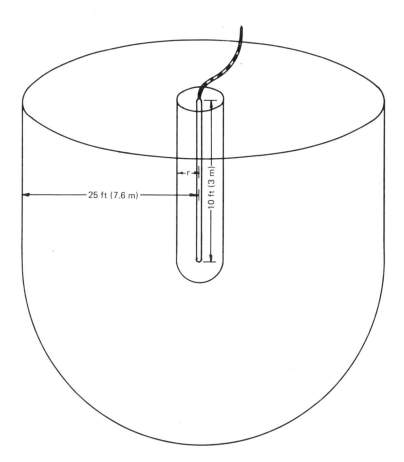

Fig 37
Electrode Resistance Development

Table 4
Electrode Resistance at a Radius r ft from a 10 ft (3 m) Long by $\frac{5}{8}$ in (16 mm) Diameter Rod
(Total Resistance at r = 25 ft (7.6 m) = 100%)

Distance from Electrode Surface r (ft)	(m)	Approximate Percentage of Total Resistance
0.1	(0.03)	25
0.2	(0.06)	38
0.3	(0.09)	46
0.5	(0.15)	52
1.0	(0.3)	68
5	(1.5)	86
10	(3.0)	94
15	(4.6)	97
20	(6.1)	99
25	(7.6)	100
(100)	(30.5)	(104)
(1000)	(30.5)	(117)

sistance at 113% for the 25 ft (7.62 m) radius value, or would be the resistance at a radius of about 500 ft (152 m).

The first few inches away from the rod are the most important ones, as far as reducing the electrode resistance is concerned. In high-soil-resistivity locations, decreasing the soil resistivity in this area, such as by chemical treatment or the use of concrete, will be most useful in improving the effectiveness of a grounding-electrode system.

Adding more electrodes to the first one, in order to reduce the resistance, does not affect the resistance close to the electrode. Out to a distance equal to half the spacing between the electrodes, the diagram and logic of Fig 37 apply. Beyond that distance, however, the area of each of the shells is less than linearly proportional to radius. So the resistance will be higher than the value obtained by dividing the resistance of a single rod by the number of rods in the grounding system, unless the rods are separated by impractically great distances.

4.1.2 Recommended Acceptable Values. The most elaborate grounding system may not perform satisfactorily unless the connection of the system to earth is adequate for the particular installation. It follows, therefore, that the earth connection is one of the most important parts of the whole grounding system. It is also the most difficult part to design.

The connection to earth, or the electrode system, needs to have a sufficiently low resistance to permit prompt operation of the circuit protective devices in the event of a ground fault, and to provide the required safety from shock to personnel who may be in the vicinity of equipment frames, enclosures, conductors, or the electrodes themselves. Logically, the lower the resistance of the grounding system, the more adequately these requirements are met. Yet, smaller installations with lower available levels of ground-fault current do not require as low a value of grounding resistance as do larger systems with their higher levels of ground-fault current. System ground resistances of less than 1Ω may be obtained by the use of a number of individual electrodes connected together. Such a low resistance may only be required for large substations or generating stations. Resistances in the 2–5 Ω range are generally found suitable for industrial plant substations and buildings and large commercial installations.

The 25Ω value noted in the National Electrical Code (NEC), ANSI/NFPA 70-1981 [1][11] applies to the maximum resis-

---

[11] The numbers in brackets correspond to those references listed in 4.5.

Table 5
Resistivity of Soils and
Resistances of Single Rods

Soil	Resistivity ($\Omega \cdot$ cm)			Resistance of $\frac{5}{8}$ in (16 mm) $\times$ 10 ft (3 m) Rod (Ω)		
	Avg	Min	Max	Avg	Min	Max
Fills, ashes, cinders, brine waste, salt marsh	2370	590	7000	8	2	23
Clay, shale, gumbo, loam	4060	340	16 300	13	1.1	54
Same, with added sand and gravel	15 800	1020	135 000	52	4	447
Gravel, sand, stones, with little clay or loam	94 000	59 000	458 000	311	195	1516

Table 6
Effect of Moisture Content on
Soil Resistivity

Moisture Content (% by weight)	Resistivity ($\Omega \cdot$ cm)	
	Top Soil	Sandy Loam
0	$>1000 \cdot 10^6$	$>1000 \cdot 10^6$
2.5	250 000	150 000
5	165 000	43 000
10	53 000	18 500
15	19 000	10 500
20	12 000	6300
30	6400	4200

Table 7
Effect of Temperature on
Soil Resistivity*

Temperature ($^\circ$C)	($^\circ$F)	Resistivity ($\Omega \cdot$ cm)
20	68	7200
10	50	9900
0 (water)	32	13 800
0 (ice)	32	30 000
-5	23	79 000
-15	14	330 000

*Sandy loam, 15.2% moisture.

tance *for a single electrode*. If a higher resistance is obtained for a single electrode, a second (paralleled) electrode is required. There is no implication that 25Ω per se is a satisfactory level for a grounding system.

4.1.3 Resistivity of Soils. It is recommended that the resistivity of the earth at the desired location of the connection be investigated. The resistivity of soils varies with the depth from the surface, the type and concentration of soluble chemicals in the soil, the moisture content, and the soil temperature. In other words, the resistivity is that of the electrolyte in the soil. The presence of surface water does not necessarily indicate low resistivity. Representative values of resistivity for general types of soils are given in Table 5. The effects of moisture and temperature are shown in Tables 6 and 7.

Table 8
Formulas for Calculation of Resistances to Ground*†

▽	Hemisphere radius a	$R = \dfrac{\rho}{2\pi a}$
•	One ground rod length L, radius a	$R = \dfrac{\rho}{2\pi L}\left(\ln\dfrac{4L}{a} - 1\right)$
• •	Two ground rods $s > L$; spacing s	$R = \dfrac{\rho}{4\pi L}\left(\ln\dfrac{4L}{a} - 1\right) + \dfrac{\rho}{4\pi s}\left(1 - \dfrac{L^2}{3s^2} + \dfrac{2\,L^4}{5\,s^4}\cdots\right)$
••	Two ground rods $s < L$; spacing s	$R = \dfrac{\rho}{4\pi L}\left(\ln\dfrac{4L}{a} + \ln\dfrac{4L}{s} - 2 + \dfrac{s}{2L} - \dfrac{s^2}{16L^2} + \dfrac{s^4}{512L^4}\cdots\right)$
—	Buried horizontal wire length $2L$, depth $s/2$	$R = \dfrac{\rho}{4\pi L}\left(\ln\dfrac{4L}{a} + \ln\dfrac{4L}{s} - 2 + \dfrac{s}{2L} - \dfrac{s^2}{16L^2} + \dfrac{s^4}{512L^4}\cdots\right)$
L	Right-angle turn of wire length of arm L, depth $s/2$	$R = \dfrac{\rho}{4\pi L}\left(\ln\dfrac{2L}{a} + \ln\dfrac{2L}{s} - 0.2373 + 0.2146\dfrac{s}{L} + 0.1035\dfrac{s^2}{L^2} - 0.0424\dfrac{s^4}{L^4}\cdots\right)$
人	Three-point star length of arm L, depth $s/2$	$R = \dfrac{\rho}{6\pi L}\left(\ln\dfrac{2L}{a} + \ln\dfrac{2L}{s} + 1.071 - 0.209\dfrac{s}{L} + 0.238\dfrac{s^2}{L^2} - 0.054\dfrac{s^4}{L^4}\cdots\right)$
+	Four-point star length of arm L, depth $s/2$	$R = \dfrac{\rho}{8\pi L}\left(\ln\dfrac{2L}{a} + \ln\dfrac{2L}{s} + 2.912 - 1.071\dfrac{s}{L} + 0.645\dfrac{s^2}{L^2} - 0.145\dfrac{s^4}{L^4}\cdots\right)$
✳	Six-point star length of arm L, depth $s/2$	$R = \dfrac{\rho}{12\pi L}\left(\ln\dfrac{2L}{a} + \ln\dfrac{2L}{s} + 6.851 - 3.128\dfrac{s}{L} + 1.758\dfrac{s^2}{L^2} - 0.490\dfrac{s^4}{L^4}\cdots\right)$
✳	Eight-point star length of arm L, depth $s/2$	$R = \dfrac{\rho}{16\pi L}\left(\ln\dfrac{2L}{a} + \ln\dfrac{2L}{s} + 10.98 - 5.51\dfrac{s}{L} + 3.26\dfrac{s^2}{L^2} - 1.17\dfrac{s^4}{L^4}\cdots\right)$
◯	Ring of wire diameter of ring D, diameter of wire d, depth $s/2$	$R = \dfrac{\rho}{2\pi^2 D}\left(\ln\dfrac{8D}{d} + \ln\dfrac{4D}{s}\right)$
—	Buried horizontal strip length $2L$, section a by b, depth $s/2$, $b < a/8$	$R = \dfrac{\rho}{4\pi L}\left(\ln\dfrac{4L}{a} + \dfrac{a^2 - \pi ab}{2(a+b)^2} + \ln\dfrac{4L}{s} - 1 + \dfrac{s}{2L} - \dfrac{s^2}{16L^2} + \dfrac{s^4}{512L^4}\cdots\right)$
⊘	Buried horizontal round plate radius a, depth $s/2$	$R = \dfrac{\rho}{8a} + \dfrac{\rho}{4\pi s}\left(1 - \dfrac{7}{12}\dfrac{a^2}{s^2} + \dfrac{33}{40}\dfrac{a^4}{s^4}\cdots\right)$
	Buried vertical round plate radius a, depth $s/2$	$R = \dfrac{\rho}{8a} + \dfrac{\rho}{4\pi s}\left(1 + \dfrac{7}{24}\dfrac{a^2}{s^2} + \dfrac{99}{320}\dfrac{a^4}{s^4}\cdots\right)$

*See Ref [4].

†Approximate formulas, including effects of images. Dimensions must be in centimeters to give resistance in ohms.

ρ = resistivity of earth in ohm–centimeters.

For 10 ft (3 m) rods of $\frac{1}{2}$, $\frac{5}{8}$, and $\frac{3}{4}$ in (12.7, 15.88, and 19.05 mm) diameters, the grounding resistance may be quickly determined by dividing the soil resistivity ρ, $\Omega \cdot$ cm, by 292, 302, and 311, respectively.

**Table 9
Multiplying Factors for Multiple Rods**

Number of Rods	F
2	1.16
3	1.29
4	1.36
8	1.68
12	1.80
16	1.92
20	2.00
24	2.16

4.1.4 Calculation of Resistance to Earth. The resistance to earth may be calculated and measured. The calculation has been simplified to a great extent by the formulas developed in [4] and presented in Table 8.

Multiple electrodes in parallel yield lower resistance to ground than a single electrode. Multiple rods are commonly used to provide the low grounding resistance required by high-capacity installations. Adding a second rod does not, however, provide a total resistance of half that of a single rod, unless the two are several rod lengths apart. A useful rule is that grounding systems of 2–24 rods placed one rod length apart in a line, hollow triangle, circle, or square will provide a grounding resistance equal to the single-rod resistance divided by the number of rods and multiplied by the factor F taken from Table 9.

Placing rods within the periphery of a square, circle, or other shape will not appreciably reduce the grounding resistance below that of the peripheral rods alone.

4.1.5 Current-Loading Capacity. One factor which should not be overlooked in designing a grounding system is the current-loading capacity of a connection to earth. The temperature and moisture conditions immediately surrounding the electrode have a direct effect on the resistivity of this section of the grounding circuit. Currents passing from the electrode into the earth will have a definite effect on these two conditions. Therefore the current-loading capacity of a connection must be analyzed from the standpoint of the nature of the grounding circuit and the types of loading which it can normally be expected to carry. Information useful in this regard for steel rods in concrete (reinforcing bars) is given in [5].

Currents of low magnitude, even if of long duration, will result in relatively little heating. The effect of heat conduction and the movement of moisture due to capillary action will maintain, in most cases, the resistivity of the earth at the electrode close to the original value.

Where the earth must dissipate high currents for short durations, no appreciable amount of heat can be dissipated by the normal process of thermal conductivity. The permissible current density for a given temperature rise is inversely proportional to the square root of the soil resistivity. The effective resistance of the earth connection therefore depends on the number of such situations that could occur in succession before stable conditions in the earth are reestablished.

Since approximately 25% of the grounding resistance of each rod electrode occurs within a 0.1 ft (0.03 m) radius of the rod surface, serious heating and vaporization of the moisture adjacent to the rods may occur on heavy faults. When the moisture is boiled away, the effectiveness of the rod in the dried-out earth is substantially reduced, and arcing below the ground surface is likely. The boiling away of soil water results in steaming or "smoking" at the ground surface near the electrode.

Ground currents of high magnitude

and long duration are unusual, but could occur as the result of ground faults that are not cleared promptly. If ground currents of this type are anticipated, the system must cover a relatively large area and employ a sufficient number of electrodes to keep the current density in the earth to a low value [10].

4.1.6 Soil Treatment. Soil resistivity may be reduced anywhere from 15 to 90%, depending upon the kind and texture of the soil, by chemical treatment. There are a number of chemicals suitable for this purpose, including sodium chloride, magnesium sulfate, copper sulfate, and calcium chloride. Common salt and magnesium sulfate are most commonly used.

Chemicals are generally applied by placing them in a circular trench around the electrode in such a manner as to prevent direct contact with the electrode. While the effects of treatment will not become apparent for a considerable period, they may be accelerated by saturating the area with water. Also, such treatment is not permanent and must be renewed periodically, depending on the nature of the chemical treatment and the characteristics of the soil.

4.2 Ground Electrodes

4.2.1 Existing Electrodes. Basically all ground electrodes may be divided into two groups. The first group comprises underground metallic piping systems, metal building frameworks, well casings, steel piling, and other underground metal structures installed for purposes other than grounding. The second group comprises made electrodes specifically designed for grounding purposes. The metal building frames are normally attached by long anchor bolts to their concrete foundation footings. The anchor bolts in concrete serve as elec-

trodes, while the metal building frame is simply a grounding conductor.

The NEC, ANSI/NFPA 70-1981 [1], states that continuous underground water or gas-piping systems in general have a resistance to earth of less than 3 Ω, and that metal building frames, local metallic underground piping systems, metal well casings, and the like have in general a resistance to earth of substantially less than 25 Ω. For safety grounding and for small distribution systems where the ground currents are of relatively low magnitude, such electrodes are usually preferred because they are economical in first cost. However, before reliance can be placed on any electrodes of this group, it is essential that their resistance to earth be measured to ensure that some unforeseen discontinuity has not seriously affected their suitability. Also, care should be exercised to ensure that all parts that might become disconnected are effectively bonded together.

4.2.2 Made Electrodes. Made electrodes may be subdivided into driven electrodes, steel reinforcing bars in below-ground concrete, buried strips or cables, grids, buried plates, and counterpoises. The type selected will depend upon the type of soil encountered and the available depth. Driven electrodes are generally more satisfactory and economical where bedrock is 10 ft (3 m) or more below the surface, while grids, buried strips, or cables are preferred for lesser depths. Grids are frequently used for substations or generating stations to provide equipotential areas throughout the entire station where hazards to life and property would justify the higher cost. They also require the least amount of buried material for a given electrode resistance. Buried plates have not been used extensively in recent years because of the high cost as compared to rods or strips. Also, when used in small numbers they are the least efficient type of made electrode. The counterpoise is a form of buried cable electrode used to ground transmission-line towers and structures (see Tables 8 and 9 and [11].

When multiple electrodes are used, spacings of less than 10 ft (3 m) do not provide the most economical use of materials.

In selecting the number and size of grounding terminals, their current-discharge limitations must be recognized. If these are exceeded, the earth around the electrode may be exploded by steam generation, or may be dried out to the extent of becoming nonconductive.

4.2.3 Driven Rod or Pipe. Driven electrodes are normally rods. Where soil conditions permit, a few deep rods are usually more satisfactory than a multiplicity of short rods, since the soil resistivity generally decreases with depth due to the increased moisture content. A number of design charts for the determination of optimum ground-rod dimensions and spacings for a given installation are given in [12].

4.2.4 Concrete-Encased Rods or Wires. Concrete below ground level is a semiconducting medium of about $3000 \Omega \cdot$ cm resistivity at $20\,^{\circ}$C, or somewhat lower than the average earth resistivity. Consequently, in earth of average or high resistivity, the encasement of rod or wire electrodes in concrete results in lower resistance than when a similar electrode is placed directly into earth. This is due to a reduction of the resistance of the material closest to the primary electrode, in much the same manner as chemical treatment of the earth reacts near the electrode. While it is seldom justifiable to excavate or drill holes for the placement of concrete for this purpose, the widespread use of steel reinforcing bars in concrete foundations and footings provides a ready-made supply of grounding electrodes at structures utilizing this type of construction. It is only necessary to bring out an adequate electrical connection from a main reinforcing bar of each such footing for attachment to the building ground bus or structural steel.

A convenient means for such a connection is to tack-weld a short connecting bar between one of the vertical reinforcing bars and one of the anchor bolts for connection above the footing surface. The steel frame of a building, attached to these anchor bolts, then becomes a highly effective grounding conductor, and is used as a grounding bus in many industrial buildings.

Each such a *footing electrode* has a resistance equal to or lower than that of a driven rod of equal depth. The large number of such footings inherent to buildings will provide a net ground resistance considerably lower than that normally provided by other made electrode methods, generally below 1 Ω and frequently of the order of 0.25 Ω.

Test results and design data for the determination of the ground resistance of single and multiple concrete-encased footing electrodes are given in [5].

Steel rods in concrete in (irregular) excavations in rock or very rocky soil have been found greatly superior to other types of made electrodes. The principles governing this electrode type are those that provide grounds for the majority of the steel towers of high-voltage transmission lines.

4.2.5 Buried Strip, Wire, and Cable. Where bedrock is near the surface, or where sand is encountered, the soil is apt to be very dry and of high resistivity, and it is necessary to have an earthing connection of considerable extent. Under such conditions, buried metal strips, wires, or cables offer the most economical solution. Since the effectiveness of this type of electrode for lightning discharges is a function of its inductance, the use of a number of well-spaced shorter strips in parallel is preferable to one or more long strips. The depth at which the strips are buried is not critical. Tests by the National Bureau of Standards [9] show that the resistance decreases only about 5%, when the burial depth is increased from 18 in to 36 in (0.5 m–1 m), based on uniform soil resistivity. Similarly the effect of conductor size is extremely small.

4.2.6 Grid System. Grid system usually extend over the entire station yard and may extend some distance beyond the boundary fence. They consist of conductors buried a minimum of 0.5 ft (0.15 m) in the ground, forming a network of squares or rectangles. The spacing of the grid conductors will vary with the voltage class of the station, but cable spacings of 10–12 ft (3.0–3.7 m) are commonly used. All cable crossings should be securely bonded and the system connected to the normal ground system as well as to all equipment and steel structures. In rock ground, where driven grounds are impractical, it is sometimes more economical and desirable to use a grid system in place of buried strips, in which case the cables are usually buried at a depth of 1–2 ft (0.3–0.6 m). The basic characteristics and design elements for extensive grid systems are given in [7].

Where the enclosing fence is within the perimeter of the buried grid, the fence must be bonded to the grid to minimize the shock hazard from the *touch potential* of persons touching the fence and, of course, standing on the ground which may be at a substantially different potential. Where the enclosing fence is

at least 4 ft (1.22 m) beyond the perimeters of the grid, the fence should be grounded to its own electrode system, which will include a cable buried in the earth approximately 3 ft (0.91 m) outside the fence line, for the same reasons as discussed. Refer to IEEE Std 80-1976 [2] for more information.

Coarse cracked rock, usually granite, is normally spread all over the surface of the soil within such a substation grid area, not for housekeeping reasons, but to provide a high-resistance surface treatment to reduce the hazard from *step potential* to persons within this area during a severe fault.

4.2.7 Plates. The preferred practice with plate electrodes is to bury them on edge since a minimum of excavation is required and it is possible to obtain better contact with the soil when backfilling. There appears to be little difference between the effective resistance of horizontal and vertical plates. For commonly used plates of 10–20 ft (0.9–1.9 m²) the optimum burial depth is 5–8 ft (1.52–2.4 m).

4.3 Methods and Techniques of Construction.

4.3.1 Choice of Rods. Ground rods are manufactured in diameters of $\frac{3}{8}$, $\frac{1}{2}$, $\frac{5}{8}$, $\frac{3}{4}$, and 1 in (9.53, 12.7, 15.88, 19.05, and 25.4 mm) and in lengths of 5–40 ft (1.5–12.2 m). For most applications, the diameters of $\frac{1}{2}$, $\frac{5}{8}$, and $\frac{3}{4}$ in (12.7, 15.88, and 19.05 mm), in lengths of 8, 10, 12, and 16 ft (2.44, 3.05, 3.66, and 4.88 m) are satisfactory. The NEC, ANSI/NFPA 70-1981 [1], specifies that rods of steel or iron shall be at least $\frac{5}{8}$ in (15.88 mm) in diameter, and that rods of nonferrous materials shall not be less than $\frac{1}{2}$ in (12.7 mm) in diameter. Copper-clad steel, one of the most common types of rods, permits driving to considerable depth without destruction of the rod itself, while the copper coat permits direct copper-to-copper connection between the ground wire and the rod. In addition to the copper-clad steel, galvanized steel rods are available.

For ease of driving, some rods are available in sections. As each section is driven toward ground level, another section is added by use of a coupling, making a continuous conductor. A removable stud will take the driving blows and avoid damage to the threads of the joint. For safety reasons, rods should be driven so that no unguarded length remains above ground.

The effect of the rod diameter on the resistance of the connection to earth is small. The diameter of the ground rod is determined mainly by the mechanical rigidity required for driving. It is advantageous to select the smallest diameter rod that meets the driving requirements. Average soil conditions will permit the use of the $\frac{1}{2}$ in (12.7 mm) rod. The $\frac{5}{8}$ in (15.88 mm) rod can be driven in nearly all types of soil, and the $\frac{3}{4}$ in (19.05 mm) rod may be reserved for exceptionally hard driving conditions or for deep driven rods.

For ordinary soil condition, the 10 ft (3 m) length of rod has become fairly well established as a minimum standard length to meet the code requirement of a minimum of 8 buried ft (2.44 buried m).

4.3.2 Methods of Driving Rods. Sledging requires a minimum of driving equipment, but may require considerable time per foot of rod. A modification of the sledging process, consisting of a chuck and sliding hammer, permits the work to be carried on at a level convenient to the worker without a ladder or auxiliary platform. An additional advantage is that the blow is delivered to the rod at a point not far from the ground line, thus permitting rods to be driven to greater depths than would be possible by hand sledging. If rods are to be driven on a comparatively large scale, it is desirable to provide power driving equipment. Electric, pneumatic, and gasoline driven hammers are available, the first two requiring sources of power. Regardless of the type of driving tool used, precautions should be taken to prevent *mushrooming* of the head.

4.3.3 Locating a Water Main (New Construction). Prior to new construction, analysis of the soil condition and location of the grounding point may permit locating a water pipe nearby. This would eliminate a long grounding line to a distant water main with its inherently high inductance. The economic advantage of such an arrangement should not be overlooked.

4.3.4 Connecting to Electrodes. Connections to electrodes are usually made by one of several means. The first of these methods involves the use of mechanical (bolted) fittings, which are readily available, simple to install, disconnectable for measurements of resistance to earth, and have a long history of satisfactory usage. Although corrosion has sometimes presented a problem, treatment of the joint as an ordinary electrical connection in a corrosive environment eliminates most of the problems in this respect. Mechanical connections should, if at all possible, be accessible for inspection and servicing.

The second method, a thermite process of connecting to the electrode, has increased in usage in recent years because of the savings in time and costs when many connections must be made. This method provides a permanent connection, eliminates contact resistance, is relatively corrosion free, and permits the use of smaller cable because of the 450 °C maximum temperature limitation, as compared to the maximum of 250 °C usually permitted for mechanical connections. (The NEC ANSI/NFPA 70-1981 [1, article 250-94] imposes a minimum conductor size limitation, however.) It does, however, have certain inherent limitations. It requires separate disconnecting means, such as aboveground bolted joints, for measurements of resistance to earth. It also requires a certain amount of training, and it cannot be used in the presence of volatile or explosive mixtures, or where the gaseous products of the operation would interfere with nearby operations.

Utilities are experimenting currently with a third method, which involves the use of a copper or copper-alloy connector which is squeezed onto both ground rod and cable simultaneously by a hydraulic press. This method is economical, presents most of the advantages of the thermite process, and eliminates most of the objections to that process.

Other methods of joining, such as brazing or welding, are satisfactory if properly done.

4.3.5 Joining to Underground Piping Systems. Joining to pipe presents several problems. Clamp-type fittings are relatively expensive, since they must obviously accommodate a large pipe in addition to the relatively small conductor. Welding or brazing to the pipe will cause localized stress, which may impair the function of the pipe, particularly if it contains fluid under high pressure.

4.3.6 Joining to Structural Steel. Bolted fittings lend themselves best to structural steel that can be field drilled but not welded. These are available in a number of shapes and sizes to accommodate the range of conductors. Material for the clamps, or protective finishes applied to the clamps should be chosen so as to be satisfactory for both the grounding wire and the steel or iron from the corrosion standpoint. Brazing and the thermite process are also used when connecting to structural steel, but should be restricted to applications that will not affect the structural properties of the steel.

4.3.7 Preparing the Joint. It is important that the surface of any connection be cleaned of any insulating medium, such as insulation, grease, paint, or dirt, before making the connection.

4.4 Measurement of Resistance to Earth.

4.4.1 Need for Measurement. In any formula for the determination of the resistance to earth there are many indeterminate factors, and too much reliance should not be placed upon the calculated results. For example, the soil resistivity varies inversely with the soil temperature and directly with the moisture content and, usually, depth. The only certain way to determine the resistance is to measure it after the system has been completed. A desirable refinement would be to measure the resistance of each electrode during installation.

4.4.2 Methods for Measuring. The principles used in the measurement of resistance to earth are essentially the same as those used for measuring other types of electrical resistances. The various methods available all make use of two auxiliary electrodes in addition to the one under test and may be grouped into the following three general classes:

(1) The three-point method, in which the resistance to earth of the electrode under test and of the auxiliary electrodes is measured two electrodes at a time, in series. This method is suitable for measuring the resistance to earth of isolated ground electrodes or small grounding installations. It is not suitable for the measurement of low-resistance installations.

(2) The fall-of-potential method, which involves passing a known alternating current through the electrode under test and one of the auxiliary electrodes, and measuring the potential drop between the former electrodes and a secondary auxiliary electrode set at various distances between the two fixed electrodes. This method may be subject to considerable error if stray ground currents are present, or if pipes or other conductors are buried near the test electrode.

(3) The ratio method, which involves measurements of the ratio of the resistance to earth of an auxiliary test electrode to the series resistance to earth of the electrode under test and a second auxiliary electrode. Multiplying this ratio by the series resistance gives the effective resistance of the ground electrodes. This method is more satisfactory than the triangulation methods since ratios of the resistance of the auxiliary test electrode to the resistance of the electrode under test may be as high as 300:1.

A more complete treatment of these three methods may be found in [6].

Commercially available portable testing instruments provide the most convenient and satisfactory means for measuring the resistance of connections to earth. Instruments used for measuring insulation resistance are not suitable, however, because they cannot measure sufficiently low resistance values. Also, ordinary low-resistance ohmmeters lack sufficient voltage for this purpose, and have no means for separating out the grounding resistance of the auxilary electrodes needed to make the test.

Precision in measurements of the resistance to earth is difficult to obtain and is usually not required. Normally, an accuracy of the order of ±25% is sufficient in view of the many variables.

It is desirable, in measuring the resistance of the completed system, to allow some time to elapse before measurements are made, so that the earth around the electrodes will be consolidated. This does not apply to the auxiliary electrodes required in the test, since their resistance is negated in the test method.

4.4.3 Periodic Testing. Tests should be made periodically after the original installation and test, so that it can be determined whether the resistance is remaining constant or is increasing. If later tests show that the resistance is increasing to an undesirable value, steps should be taken to reduce the resistance either by additional electrodes, by increasing the moisture content, or by chemical treatment.

4.4.4 Earth Resistivity Measurements. The commercial portable instruments available for measuring the grounding electrode resistance normally may be used to measure the soil resistivity as well. For this purpose they are connected to four short electrodes spaced uniformly in a line. Spacing between the two center electrodes is a direct measure of the effective depth desired for the resistivity, that is, for example, a 10 ft (3 m) spacing will yield the average resistivity of the top 10 ft (3 m) of soil, and so on.

The instrument yields an ohmic reading, which then, multiplied by 2 times the spacing in centimeters, is the soil resistivity in $\Omega \cdot cm$. Full instructions for this test are provided with each test instrument.

4.4.5 Cathodic Protection. Discussion of cathodic protection is beyond the scope of this document. For information see [3], [8].

4.5 References

[1] ANSI/NFPA 70-1981, National Electrical Code.

[2] IEEE Std 80-1976, Guide for Safety in AC Substation Grounding.

[3] COLEMAN, W.E., and FROSTICK, H. Electrical Grounding and Cathodic Protection at the Fairless Works. Presented by the AIEE Subcommittee on Cathodic Protection at the 1954 AIEE Winter General Meeting.

[4] DWIGHT, H.B. Calculation of Resistance to Ground. *AIEE Transactions*, vol 55, Dec 1936, pp 1319–1328.

[5] FAGAN, E.J., and LEE, R.H. The Use of Concrete Enclosed Reinforcing Rods as Grounding Electrodes. *IEEE Transactions on Industry and General Applications*, vol IGA-6, July/Aug 1970, pp 337–348.

[6] FINK, D.G., and CARROLL, J.M., Eds. *Standard Handbook for Electrical Engineers*. New York: McGraw-Hill Book Company, 1968.

[7] GROSS, E.T.B., CHITNIS, B.V., and STRATTON, L.J. Grounding Grids for High-Voltage Stations. *AIEE Transactions (Power Apparatus and Systems)*, vol 72, Aug 1953, pp 799–810.

[8] HEADLEE, J.F. Cathodic Protection for Steel Mill Grounding Systems. *Iron and Steel Engineer*, Mar 1954.

[9] PETERS, O.S. Ground Connections for Electric Systems. Technical Bulletin 108, National Bureau of Standards, Boulder, CO.

[10] RUDENBERG, R. Grounding Principles and Practice—I: Fundamental Considerations on Ground Currents. *Electrical Engineering*, vol 64, Jan 1945, pp 1–13.

[11] TAGG, G.F. *Earth Resistances*. London WC2: George Newnes Ltd, Tower House, Southampton St.

[12] ZABORSKY, J., and RITTENHOUSE, J.W. Design Charts for Determining Optimum Ground-Rod Dimensions. *AIEE Transactions (Power Apparatus and Systems)*, vol 72, Aug 1953, pp 810–817.

Index

Switch
  disconnecting, 39
  open disconnect, 38
  primary and secondary, 39
Switching centers, 77
System neutral
  grounding
    ground-fault-neutralizer, 26, 27, 29, 30
    reactance, 26, 27, 29
    resistance, 26, 27, 28, 29, 30
    solid, 26, 27, 28
System
  dc, 48
  dc power, 48
  equipment grounding, 48, 49, 75
  four wire, 44
  grounded neutral, 20, 27, 31, 41
  grounding conductor, 65, 81
  high-resistance grounded, 44
  interior wiring, 62, 70
  low resistance, 39
  low resistance grounded neutral, 41
  low voltage, 21, 30, 34
  metal piping, 75
  overcurrent protection, 47, 50, 63
  power, 43
  power transmission and distribution, 43
  reactance grounded, 37
  resistance grounded, 28, 37, 38, 39
  resonant grounded, 30
  safety, 21, 22
  three phase, 56

T

Time modulation current choppers, 57
Terminal apparatus, 81
Transformer
  autotransformer, 43
  current, 35, 36
  distribution, 44
  grounding
    T-connected, 31

  wye-delta, 31, 33, 35, 37
  zigzag, 31, 32
  industrial substation, 26
  multiple, 39
  power, 25, 26, 38, 43
  single phase, 31
  single-phase distribution class, 32
  unit connected, 43

V

Voltage
  hazards, abnormal, 23
  third harmonic, 44
  three phase, 31
  primary, 44
  withstand, 67
  zero sequence, 31
Voltage drop
  impedance (IZ), 48
  inductive, 57, 58
  phase conductor, 51
  reactive, 51
  resistive, 55
  round trip, 54
  round-trip zero-sequence, 56
  shock-exposure, 54
Voltage gradient, surface, 67

W

Wiring, building-interior, 75

Z

Zero-potential difference
  concept, 76
  condition, 75
Zero-sequence
  current, 37, 56
  current transformer, 31, 35, 36
  inductive reactance, 37
  isolation, 35
  resistance, 37
  voltage, 31